Hebridean Heroines

Hebridean Heroines

Twentieth Century Queen's Nurses
(1940s – 1970s)

Catherine M. Morrison

Islands Book Trust

Published in 2017 by the Islands Book Trust

www.islandsbooktrust.org

© Islands Book Trust 2017

ISBN: 978-1-907443-73-2

Text © Catherine M. Morrison

The Islands Book Trust would like to thank Donnie Morrison
for his assistance in the publication of this volume.

Islands Book Trust
Laxay Hall
Laxay
Isle of Lewis
HS2 9PJ
Tel: 01851 830316

Typeset by Erica Schwarz (www.schwarz-editorial.co.uk)
Cover design by Raspberry Creative Type, Edinburgh
Printed and bound by Martins the Printers, Berwick upon Tweed

To Angus, Catriona and Euan

Contents

Foreword

Contemporary community nurses work in a rapidly changing world which their forebears would hardly recognise – but there is so much to inspire them in the remarkable courage, dedication and self-sacrifice demonstrated by their Queen's Nurse forebears in the Outer Hebrides. Thanks to Catherine Morrison their unique testimonies have been recorded and preserved.

At first glance, their roles seem worlds apart. The community nurse is no longer on her own. Most now work in complex inter-professional teams. Initiatives across the United Kingdom are clear that the current hospital based system of health care is unsustainable and undesirable. With a growing population of people living with multiple long term conditions, the demand for care and support is increasing. And the need for community nursing expertise has never been greater.

People are being supported with sophisticated aids and equipment aids to stay at home with acute and complex health needs. In many areas of Scotland, advanced nurse practitioners are working alongside district nurses to deliver care at home, which in the past would have been given in hospital. Alongside this, district nurses are becoming more involved in anticipatory care, working with individuals and their families to consider options and clearly document preferences for what matters most to people and their future care needs.

Health visitors are the first point of contact for all families with children under five. They are also at the forefront of addressing the public health challenges of childhood, including the prevention of obesity. The expertise of community mental health and learning disability nurses are in demand as people live longer with a range of health and wellbeing challenges.

Technology has come on in leaps and bounds. Instead of a static home phone, community nurses now have mobile tablets and digital pens to help them do their jobs. But the vocation of nursing is still founded on the same principles and the challenges of delivering the best care in the most remote areas also remain the same. And the Queen's Nursing Institute Scotland is still there to support them.

The Institute is still in Castle Terrace; it has been reconstituted as the Queen's Nursing Institute Scotland, now a charitable organisation. It exists to promote excellence in community nursing to improve the health and well-being of the people of Scotland. Our purpose is to enable nurses who work in Scotland's communities to be the very best they can be. We have a proud tradition and clear set of values as a foundation for contemporary community nursing excellence.

In 2015 the Institute agreed to reintroduce the Queen's Nurse title to Scotland. It will be awarded to clinical nurse leaders who can demonstrate their impact as expert practitioners. There will be a rigorous assessment process and an inspiring development programme. Whether they are adult nurses, mental health nurses, learning disability nurses, midwives or health visitors they will act as catalysts for change in the communities of Scotland.

We are following the example of our colleagues in the Queen's Nursing Institute (constituted as a separate charity to cover England, Northern Ireland, Wales) which currently has more than 700 Queen's Nurses. They have a growing reputation for influencing policy nationally and locally as Queen's Nurses. We hope to build on this reputation with a particular emphasis on public health, inequalities and integrated working with Scotland's communities.

We are incredibly proud to be carrying on a tradition of extraordinary nursing as practised by these remarkable nurses in the Outer Hebrides. And we look forward to highlighting the work of modern day heroines and heroes – the new Queen's Nurses.

Clare Cable
Chief Executive and Nurse Director,
Queen's Nursing Institute Scotland

Introduction

The middle decades of the twentieth century were, in Britain, a time of social and economic recovery. The two world wars had devastated a society which was only just emerging from the turmoil of agrarian and industrial revolutions. In the country's furthest reaches – the Western Isles – a tough and resourceful people had carved a rugged lifestyle based on the natural resources of land and sea. The Outer Hebrides are now, since the construction of bridges and causeways and the introduction of effective air transport, very closely integrated with mainstream Scottish culture and society. But in the mid-twentieth century they were a world apart; a world of close-knit communities, age-old crafts and skills, and deep religious devotion.

One aspect of Hebridean society was remarkable for being well in advance of its time. The Highlands and Islands Medical Service, established in 1913, was providing healthcare of the highest quality to the people of this remote area. It was part of a powerful British tradition which had driven the foundation of many nursing services across the world, including the Victorian Order of Nurses of Canada, and the Australian Bush Nursing Service. And it had its roots in a remarkable organisation: The Queen's Nursing Institute Scotland (QNIS) founded in 1889. The QNIS prided itself on training the best district nurses in the world, taking young women who had already experienced the rigours of Britain's nurse training schools and putting them through a tough and challenging programme of further preparation which both extended their clinical skills and instilled a sense of resourcefulness and inventiveness. The process produced a group of women who were able to provide high quality care in both the most deprived inner cities and the hardiest of rural terrains. Among them were the nurses who cared for the islanders of the Outer Hebrides, putting their skills at the service of a population that, just decades before, had been deprived of even the most basic healthcare.

What was so impressive about the Queen's Nurses of the Outer Hebrides was their capacity not only to bring fundamental nursing skill to their patients but also to demonstrate the ability to improvise, to push the boundaries of their practice when needed, and to work closely with the communities they served, winning the respect and affection of all. Now that this book is bringing their poignant and moving stories to a wide readership, I hope that their personal testimony may help inspire a new generation of nurses to understand the true potential of their work – the ways in which expert nursing practice, coupled with commitment and courage, can transform people's lives.

Christine E. Hallett
November 2016

Author's Preface

I believe the nurses who feature in this book should be described as heroines! This term had already been used by Mrs Christine MacLennan, a District Nursing Officer, before the 1970s. She maintained that, '[nurses] had to have the courage and the physical strength to face the black moor walks at night, exhausting battles with wind and rain and journeys by small boats across stormy seas. It was the way help must come to save the patient, it was given without hesitation.'

This is the story of a remarkable group of nurses working in one of the most remote areas of Europe and of the service they gave over four decades from the 1940s to the 1970s. Until now it has been an untold story. It is related by the nurses themselves and details their trials and tribulations, professional and personal challenges, everyday joys and blessings, routine frustrations and occasional deep despair.

The role of district nurses in these far outlying islands of Europe was certainly unique. Their stories show them as remarkably brave and resilient women, one of the standard definitions of heroism. But that is the last thing they would say about themselves, who 'were only doing their job'. They did not recoil when called upon to carry out work which was physically and mentally taxing, often alone with no peer support. They just regarded it as 'their work'.

One nursing historian has suggested that nursing by its very nature is potentially heroic because effective nurses engage with the physical damage and emotional distress of patients. The nurses of the Outer Hebrides described engaging in both. They repeatedly demonstrated great strength of character, care and concern for others, and real courage in the face of danger.

Island life imposed geographical isolation but not insularity in outlook. These women were highly-trained Queen's Nurses and were able to maintain and update their skills. Their predecessors had inspired a new model of district nurse midwifery in Kentucky and other parts of the world. They provided constant and continuous care every day of the year, from the moment of birth to the last days of life. That is why they were widely regarded as the 'Bee's Knees'.

Author's Note

While working as a district nurse I encountered many patients who had been district nurses themselves and had stories to relate about their life and work, which I felt was part of the unique history of the Outer Hebrides and nursing. Then when I retired I became a Queen's Nurse Visitor (visiting Queen's Nurses who are over eighty years old) and again was in contact with women whose stories about their working lives inspired me. I began to interview them and this book is the result. These stories are important, not only because many of the women are no longer here, but also because they recall a lifestyle that cannot be recognised today. To capture the history of these nurses was an honour and many of the experiences they related will stay with me forever. This book is both my thanks to them and their legacy. It is also the first time this aspect of social history in the Outer Hebrides has been explored.

Some of the nurses, although willing 'to tell their story', preferred to remain anonymous. I have given fictional names to those who wished to preserve their anonymity, however their stories remain just as important.

Acknowledgements

This book has had a long family gestation spanning retirement, two family weddings and three grandchildren. Thanks to my family: Maryann, Kate and Aonghas, Aileen and Paul, and my husband Allan for their patience and support. Thanks to Aonghas Smith, Canada for the amazing graphics for this book.

Thanks go to Professor Christine Hallett and Dr Hannah Cooke, Manchester University for their continued encouragement to write this book. Thanks to Chris Holme for his editing and assistance in turning what was an academic thesis into a readable book. I also owe thanks to the Queen's Nursing Institute Scotland for financial assistance and in particular to Claire Cable, Nurse Director, for her advice and support.

Thanks also to the many others who helped me along the way, such as David and Eunice, Annetta, Isobel, Rena and Jessie for their encouragement and Christine for transcribing the interviews.

Finally, my thanks go to the nurses in this book who gave me their memories, which I will never forget.

CHAPTER ONE

District Nursing: How it Started

Mr Rathbone

Origins

Nursing the sick and caring for them at home has been customary since the beginning of human society. Until the late eighteenth century the lay nurse carried out many roles in the community such as handywoman, corpse washer or midwife and could be practising bleeding or blistering, among many other tasks. In 1840 Elizabeth Fry founded a Protestant organisation that later became known as the 'Institute of Nursing Sisters' because she felt that 'there was a necessity for a class of women to attend upon the sick different from the hireling nurses that are generally obtained'.

The debate regarding the social class of nurses continued throughout the Victorian era and had its roots in views about the class and role of working women. With the emancipation of women and their movement into paid occupations the training of district nurses became established. At this time a small number of women were entering the medical profession, signifying a wider movement towards reform in the education of women. Florence Nightingale was ambivalent about the role of Elizabeth Garrett, the first female doctor, asserting 'Let women begin with the Profession (midwifery) which is undoubtedly theirs'. Yet she also suggested that 'whether it is right or wrong that women should enter medicine, shall we not do more harm than good in shutting them out?' Although Nightingale's argument may have

1

been more about her views on the professions of women, she also had an opinion regarding the qualities required to be a nurse. She accepted that district nurses would require a higher standard of character and skills, which would have the unfortunate effect of excluding working class candidates.

It is difficult to discuss the history of district nursing without a mention of the notorious fictional characters of Sarah Gamp and her colleague Betsy Prig portrayed by Dickens. Their pictures have been widely publicised over the years to typify the nurses found in nineteenth-century private nursing and St Bartholomew's Hospital London. Dickens described nurses 'as those women who care for the sick by neglecting them, stealing from them and at times physically abusing them'. However in 1989 an influential article was published in the journal 'Victorian Studies' which presented a different view of Sarah Gamp, saying 'her character was destroyed, she was vilified as no doctor ever was for expecting to be paid for her work: her professional autonomy was undermined, most important of all her skills were denigrated or ignored. She had more expertise than many hospital nurses and in some cases as much as male medical practitioners'. If this view is to be believed a great deal of damage has been done to the history of nursing, which frequently portrays Sarah Gamp and her like as the characters from which the profession developed.

Florence Nightingale.
(© National Portrait
Gallery, London)

A Victorian postcard of the gin-soaked Gamp and Prig. (© The Trustees of the British Museum)

District nursing is often said to have had its beginnings in Britain in 1859, when William Rathbone, a Liverpool philanthropist, impressed by the care that the nurse Mrs Robinson gave to his wife when she was terminally ill, decided to provide nursing for the city's poor. In fact, care had previously been provided in the home by Catholic societies and deaconesses in some European settings and this may have provided a model for district nursing. Some historians maintain that Britain owed the reform of nursing to the Protestant Institute of Deaconesses at Kaiserwerth in Germany, which influenced British nurses such as Florence Nightingale.

After Mrs Rathbone's death, her husband employed Mrs Robinson to go into the poorest districts of Liverpool, where people could not afford care, to try to nurse people in their own homes. A month later Mrs Robinson returned, distressed at the conditions she saw in the community, and had to be persuaded by Rathbone to continue, which she did for four years. It was clear that little could be achieved by one nurse so Rathbone enlisted the help of the Victorian pioneer of nursing, Florence Nightingale, to set up a nursing school in the Royal Infirmary, Liverpool.

Once the nurses were district trained, Liverpool was divided into eighteen geographical districts and nurses were attached to an area to work, with a 'Lady Superintendent' providing supervision. Members of wealthy families assisted with the funding of the nursing scheme, and were often voluntary members of the committees which ran the district nursing associations. By the late nineteenth century most of the superintendents were trained nurses. From Liverpool, district nursing spread to other industrial cities, for instance, Manchester in 1864, Derby in 1865 and Leicester in 1867. St Patrick's Home for district nurses in Dublin was founded in 1876. The Glasgow Sick Poor Private Nursing Association was established in 1875 when the city also became the first location for district nurse training in Scotland.

Two significant events in nursing history which impacted on all nurses were the 1902 Midwives Act and the Nurses Registration Act of 1919, which introduced state registration of nurses and midwives. The Midwives Act however did not apply to Scotland, for which another Act was passed in 1915 (largely because of the loss of doctors and nurses for war service) when the Central Midwives Board for Scotland (CMB) was established to regulate the training and practice of midwives. In the period when the Act only applied to England, midwives from Scotland went to London to sit the examination to be placed on the midwives roll.

The Nurse Registration Act was passed in 1919 allowing each UK country to set up its own General Nursing Council (GNC) with duties to compile a syllabus of subjects for examination and to compile a register of qualified nurses. With the introduction of the registration of nurses, it was suggested that there was a time when a varied group of people were engaged in the practice of nursing. Ladies with 'excellent instruction' and servant girls with a minimum of training belonged to the same occupation and the standard of nurse training was also diverse. By 1925 the first state examinations for nurses were held. By the 1940s most nurses working in the community were not only registered but were also registered midwives and Queen's Nurses.

The advent of the NHS in 1948 brought significant changes. Patients were discharged to their homes more quickly and more acutely ill patients had to be cared for by the district staff. The work of the district nurse increased and radically changed during this period. Working conditions gradually improved and the recommended working week was reduced from forty-eight hours in 1949 to forty in 1972. Holidays were also longer and by the mid-seventies nursing staff could no longer be dismissed when they married. Problems nevertheless continued with the provision of education to all nurses.

Queen's Nurses

With the recognition of the emerging district nursing service, Queen Victoria (on the celebration of her Jubilee in 1887) provided a grant of £70,000 from the Queen Victoria Women's Jubilee Fund to be used for providing the 'training, support, maintenance and supply of nurses for the sick poor, as well as establishing training homes, supervising centres, cooperating with other bodies and established branches as necessary'. A Royal Charter in 1889 constituted the Queen Victoria Jubilee Institute for Nursing with a president and council to take charge of the annual fund.

The early stages and organisation of the scheme were fraught with problems as debate ensued in the national and nursing press as well as with the main people involved, Florence Nightingale, William Rathbone and Florence Sarah Craven, who published a Guide to District Nursing and Home Nursing in 1889. The debate

*The Queen's Nursing Headquarters
in Castle Terrace, Edinburgh.
(Royal College of Nursing)*

*Florence Sarah Craven.
(Wellcome Images)*

centred on how the grant should be used, whether another nursing organisation for nurses was required, and the differing education of nurses.

Training of Queen's Nurses included sanitary reform, health promotion, ventilation, drainage, water supply, diet for the healthy and the sick, the feeding of infants and the care of the new-born with some of these subjects unfamiliar to trained hospital nurses. It was also noted that nurses were also advised 'to read Mrs Craven's excellent manual'. Considering that in the late nineteenth century, nursing was still based on a medical model, it reveals Mrs Craven as one of the pioneers for district nursing.

Florence Craven was herself a trained nurse and carried out most of the investigative work for a report into district nursing in the London area in 1875. She was particularly scathing about the care that was being provided. As a result of the findings of the survey it was accepted that there was a need for superior educated, trained nurse superintendents to oversee the provision of nursing care. Many feel that Florence Craven must be seen as the true originator of professional district nursing. Florence Nightingale was said to have described her as a 'genius of nursing'.

The Queen Victoria Jubilee Institute for Nursing changed its name in 1928 and was known as The Queen's Institute of District Nursing. In Scotland the history of Queen's Nurses was similar to that of England with the District Nursing Associations becoming affiliated to the Queen's Nursing Institute in 1889 when conditions were laid down for training and organisation of Queen's Nurses. A Scottish Council

A Royal visitor to Castle Terrace in 1929: the future Queen Elizabeth was president of the Institute as Duchess of York between 1928 and 1935. (Royal College of Nursing)

was established, whose president was Queen Victoria's daughter Princess Louise. In Glasgow a Sick, Poor and Private Nursing Association was already in existence, which had been founded by Mrs Mary Higgenbotham, who is believed to be the pioneer of district nursing in Scotland.

Nurse training was initially to be at an approved hospital for at least a year, followed by training in district nursing for six months, including the nursing of mothers and infants after childbirth. Nurses who worked in country districts required three months training in midwifery. The first training school in Scotland was located in Glasgow and accepted nurses for Queen's training, with other geographical areas such as Edinburgh and Dundee becoming Queen's Nurse training branches. Most nurses featured in this book were required to complete their three-year general training and usually a year's midwifery training before being accepted in a Queen's training centre. The Queen's Nursing Institute was an important influence on district nursing in the Outer Hebrides.

Queen's Nurse outside Castle Terrace, Edinburgh. (Royal College of Nursing)

The following are examples of examination questions from various years to assess whether the nurse was 'fit to be a Queen's Nurse':

1948 – What help apart from your nursing care might you be able to obtain for a necessitous patient recovering from hemiplegia? From what sources could this help be obtained?

1950 – For what kind of disease have you seen the following prescribed:

    a) Streptomycin

    b) Morphine.

    Describe the procedure when giving one of these medicines in the patient's home?

1952 – You are called in to nurse a patient who has been discharged from hospital after two years' treatment with poliomyelitis. He has paralysis of both his legs and is alone in the house from 8am until 5pm. Describe the plans you would make for his care.

1952 – What part can the district nurse play in the National Campaign against accidents in the home? Give examples of the commoner home accidents and show how these might be prevented.

1956 – A young miner suffering from paraplegia following a severe spinal injury is brought home after months in hospital. Describe the nursing care and social care that he would need to make his life happier and fuller.

1956 – What advice would a district nurse give to a wife whose husband had pulmonary tuberculosis and is being nursed at home pending his admission to hospital? They have two small children at home.

1957 – What would you do if called to the following emergencies?

    a) A diabetic patient in a coma

    b) A child with a cut hand that is bleeding badly

    c) A man who has tried to commit suicide by putting his head in a gas oven

1957 – The doctor has asked you to visit immediately a man who has just had a cerebral thrombosis. You arrive to find the patient semi-conscious on the kitchen floor fully clothed and his wife and married son very upset. What would you do for this patient? What equipment would be needed and how would you obtain this?

1957 – Discuss the responsibilities of the district nurses in regards to:

    Dangerous drugs

    Care of nursing equipment

    The house, furniture and car provided by the local Health Authority for her own use

    Her own health

Not only did the nurse have to care for the patients, she had responsibility for drugs, equipment and her home and car, which did not belong to her. It is interesting that the nurse was also taught about the necessity of looking after her own health. It is unlikely that present day nurses have seen conditions such as tuberculosis and poliomyelitis which would have required a great deal of nursing care. The examination papers provide an awareness of the medical conditions that were prevalent at that time as well as the drugs that were in use.

The following examples were examination questions, and their answers, from nurses who worked over thirty years before the nurses in this book:

1915 – *Question:* If sent to attend an urgent operation for strangulated hernia, how would you prepare the patient and the room?

Answer: I should instruct the people to light the copper, for plenty of boiling water, and boil the basins and also see that a fire is put in the patient's room. I should do any necessary dusting with a cloth wrung out in Lysol. The abdomen and as much of the patient as possible should be washed and warm stockings put on.

1915 – *Question:* Give an account of the ways in which typhoid can be carried?

Answer: Typhoid can be carried by milk from a milkman who gets his milk from an unsanitary farm; by water, where water pipes run side to side with drainage pipes that are faulty. Shallow wells may be a sources of infection as well as stored rain water. Cistern water in houses where the water closet has no separate system. Typhoid may also be spread by the nurse or attendant through urine, excreta, perspiration, clothing from the bed, feeding cups and any utensil used by the patient and not carefully disinfected.

1917 – *Question:* How would you make a patient understand why bread, meat and sugar must be saved and how to help her divide and plan the amount allowed so that the children and husband shall be adequately nourished?

Answer: Tell the patient in simple language that our common supply of food is largely obtained from abroad and that on account of the submarine menace and the amount needed to keep the troops in fit condition the quantities available for civilians are very much lessened. She can be told to use ground and whole rice, oatmeal, tapioca, lentil, maize flour, dates and any available dried cereals and also cheese and fish. Root vegetables such as carrots, parsnips, swedes and turnips can also be used. The housewife should be encouraged to use the above mentioned foodstuffs in place of bread, meat and sugar so as to keep within the amount allowed by the Food Controller.

1918 – *Question:* What are the chief nursing points to be observed in a case of rheumatic fever that has to be nursed in a small labourer's cottage?

Answer: Wool and bandages must be applied to all painful joints as they become affected: the patient should have a flannel gown and lie between blankets except for a draw sheet. Strict measures should be taken in order that the patient should not get out of bed or even sit up on account of the strain that is already being put upon the heart by the rheumatic germ and the fever. Temperature, pulse and respiration must be taken twice daily. On account of the profuse perspiration the patient will need to be sponged frequently. Milk and water or barley water should be given in large quantities and no beef tea … the friends should be warned that the patient will need close and careful attention for four to six weeks.

1918 – Question: In a country district you are called to see a 'gathered finger'; you find serious swelling and pain involving hand and arm. What steps should you take pending doctors' orders?

Answer: The finger should first be soaked in some antiseptic lotion, the pus squeezed out and the wound made as clean as possible. A fermentation should then be put on and the arm placed in a sling, care being taken that the hand is raised no higher than the elbow. The patient must be sent without delay to see his doctor or go to the nearest hospital.

It is clear that the training was comprehensive and consistent with the health problems of the time that the nurses worked. It is no wonder that the Queen's nursing movement provided a model for many other countries to follow.

District nursing spread rapidly in English speaking countries overseas. The Victorian Order for Canada was founded in 1897, while in Australia the 'Bush' Nursing Association was set up in 1911. In New Zealand, an Act of 1909 allowed for visiting nurses in the rural areas, while in the USA, the National Organisation for Public Health Nursing was started in 1912 through the Boston District Nursing Association, which dated from 1886.

Remote area nursing in the Australian bush originated in Victoria, where it was provided for more than 100 years, following a similar model to that of the remote district nursing service in Britain. Some smaller geographical areas did not have access to home-based nursing, apart from what could be obtained privately. Queensland, for example, did not have an organised district nursing service until the 1960s.

In Canada an experienced 'lady nurse superintendent' was sent with the first nurses to the Klondike in 1898. It is probable that the Canadian nurses were taking advice from the British Queen's nursing system. Many areas in Canada are similar to Scotland's remote and rural areas, with their mountains, small islands and rugged terrain. Labrador, which is even more remote, is an example in which a nurse's geographical area encompassed the scattered hamlets of fishermen during and after the Second World War.

Other European countries such as Norway, Finland and Denmark also faced problems with remoteness. A nurse from Denmark in the 1930s noted that 'when working in hospital responsibility is shared by many, but district nursing in lonely places in the fjords – there one's abilities are put to the test'. The nurses in this book could relate to this comment.

Working in remote areas presented challenges for health professionals worldwide. In the European countries development of district nursing was different. In rural Norway for example, nurses were employed to care for the sick in their homes and do public health work part-time from the late nineteenth century onwards. In the

1930s they began to leave the rural areas for hospital work with better prospects and more holidays and time off. Despite the trials of remote area working for health professionals worldwide, even in the twenty-first century, a study in Australia found that nurses working in these areas reported a great deal of satisfaction with the scope and circumstance of their practice. Nevertheless, nurses working in remote and rural areas have always faced different difficulties to their counterparts in urban areas, such as isolation and transport problems.

The nurses in this book recall events which occurred in the twentieth century in remote and rural areas, yet it is clear that even in the twenty-first century there are problems with delivering health care remotely.

On the Islands

The first Lewis Hospital in Stornoway, with a bed capacity of fifteen, was opened in 1896 at a cost of £2,000, funded by the community. Prior to the opening of the hospital a bequest of £1,000 from Lady Ashburton was the means of providing a district nurse and a 'Bible woman' to care for the sick in the town area of Stornoway. At the time there were already a number of 'knowledgeable women' who assisted with midwifery. The hospital itself was funded for fifty years by the local community and initially their own local general practitioner cared for the patients.

'Bible women' were the initiative of Ellen Ranyard, a missionary and social worker in London around 1857. She believed in the importance of deepening people's religious knowledge as well as caring for their health. After three months' training in a general hospital, and then midwifery training, the 'Bible woman nurse' as she was then known, was allocated a district to work in. It would appear that the 'Bible woman' in Lewis was not nurse trained, but provided a similar function to those in London, which was mainly social work. As for the district nurse in the Lewis Hospital, her duties were carried out in the hospital and the community.

The Second Report of the Lewis Hospital (1898) announced the first appointment of a Queen's Nurse to the joint offices of the hospital and the district, and that the nurse was carrying out work in the town area of Stornoway, with patients being supplied with clothing and food from the hospital when necessary. Training of nurses was introduced shortly after the hospital opened and with the addition of students the staff gradually increased. The training involved a year's instruction supported by parish councils, later increased to two years, followed by a period of midwifery training carried out in mainland hospitals. In 1899 the Lewis Hospital was reporting that a local candidate would train under the auspices of the Queen Victoria Jubilee Institute for Nursing.

The first appointment of a nurse to a rural area was reported in 1895 with the nurse's salary being paid by the Ladies' Highland Association and the Lewis District Committee. According to the report of the Local Medical Officer of Health the advantages of the district nursing service became so apparent that new appointments were made and even before the Highlands and Islands Medical Service was introduced in 1912, there were nine district nurses in Lewis. Although an application had been submitted for cars for nurses in some areas, the proposal was withdrawn due to financial constraints.

In 1917 it was noted in the Report that there were thirteen district nurses working throughout the island of Lewis, four of them being Queen's Nurse trained. The report goes on to say 'it would be difficult to overestimate the service rendered by the district nurses, for example the mortality among the new-born has been greatly reduced and puerperal disease has also greatly diminished'.

By 1934 there were nineteen district nurses, seventeen of these being Queen's Nurses, with the 'mode of conveyance used by district nurses being the bicycle, and two of the "heaviest" districts, Back and Gravir, provided with a motor cycle'. It was recognised that the bicycles were 'not really satisfactory' for the districts in Lewis. In Harris the Local Association's reply to a nurse who requested a new bicycle was 'in view of the alleged defects of the cycle these dangerous hills should not be cycled'. In other words, the blame for the broken bicycle was its misuse by the nurse!

The Lewis Hospital Report on the district nursing service in 1947 indicated that there were twenty-one district nurses employed in Lewis. It stated that 'the district nurses service was one of the most efficient and harmoniously run parts of the County Council's Public Health Department'. The Report also noted that they were 'keenly alive to the importance of improving the service by the provision of telephones and cars'. It was not until the 1950s, when the nurses in this book were working, that cars and telephones were supplied for the use of district nurses in all areas of the Outer Hebrides.

The 1940s and 1950s saw a great deal of progress for nurses' welfare in the Outer Hebrides. Telephones were installed in most nurses' cottages in the 1950s, and many nurses had cars, the first being delivered in 1936. Despite the progress the local Nursing Sub-Committee appeared to hold a great deal of control over the nurses as indicated in their notes of 1940, when they refused to allow nurses to attend a week's refresher course in tuberculosis, regardless of the Advisory Committee for Tuberculosis being willing to fund travelling expenses. One of the reasons given was that holiday arrangements had already been completed for most districts, and nurses could only attend courses immediately before or after their annual leave.

Notes of the Sub-Committee for the 1940s also show the frequent turnover of staff. When a district nurse was required for a geographical area, the Queen's Nursing

A Hebridean Queen's Nurse. As well as the hills there were the dogs to contend with when on a bike.

Institute was contacted. They supplied a list of nurses available, which could be up to seven candidates for the Local Association and Sub-Committee to choose from. However, in 1944, it was recorded that the number of nurses applying for district nurse training had been disappointing and that had it not been for the married nurses continuing to work and others who had re-joined the service, the shortage would have been serious.

Midwifery

We can date the beginning of the development of the registered midwives to the implementation of the Midwives' Institute in 1886. The pioneer of midwifery, Dame Rosalind Paget and her uncle William Rathbone (the initiator of district nursing) gave advice and help in the setting up of the Institute.

The Midwives Act of 1902 gave trained midwives status, protected the title of midwife and allowed the midwives to work independently of a doctor. It did not give the midwife the authority to issue any medical certificate, such as for a stillbirth. Dame Rosalind Paget (1855–1948), who was a leader of the Midwives Institute in the 1890s, maintained that the clause was inserted to 'make the medical practitioner happy', as there was some antagonism from the medical profession regarding the training of midwives. Paget was not concerned about this issue as at the time there was no legal requirement to register stillbirths. The Act of 1902 did not apply to

Dame Rosalind Paget.
(Wellcome Images)

Scotland until 1916, when ironically, the Central Midwives Board for Scotland had the power to suspend midwives who broke the rules, which the English Board was unable to do until the Second Midwives Act of 1918.

The Act required midwives to be trained by undertaking a diploma by examination and then become registered to practice. The third Midwives Act in 1926 followed by another Midwives Act 1936 ensured that all women in Britain were entitled to care by well-trained midwives. The creation of the NHS in 1948 also made a difference to the quality of health care, including midwifery provision.

Although women's experience of childbirth apparently improved because of the introduction of the NHS and other advances in health care, writers who carried out an oral history of midwives who had practised during the 1940s and 1950s suggest that it was the Midwives Acts which had more impact on midwives' lives than the introduction of the NHS.

The period from the 1940s until the 1960s has often been referred to as the 'golden age of district midwifery' because midwives were competent and confident and due to their training worked as autonomous professionals. The concept of a 'golden age' can fail to take into consideration the failings of a particular service. In this case the age was seen as 'golden' because midwives had more control of normal childbirth than either before or since. As we shall see later, there were drawbacks to working during the 'golden age'.

The Central Midwives Board (CMB) for Scotland produced Rules for Midwives in 1939 and 1950, which would govern practice of the participants in this book. The Rules stipulated that all midwives should attend a refresher course at intervals of not more than seven years. Within the rule book were 'Forms required under the Rules' to be completed as Notification to the CMB. An example was 'having laid out a dead body' which asks for details of the deceased and the cause of death. The Form was then sent to the Local Supervising Authority. The midwife, after her attendance at a death, was in some circumstances not allowed to deliver a baby for a period of forty-eight hours. As all of the nurses in this book carried out midwifery and general nursing, it questions whether the nurses were successful in adhering to this particular rule. They were also lone workers and would not be able to call on a colleague for help.

Her training made such an impression on midwife Chrissie Henderson, that she could still recite a poem she had had to write and learn some fifty years before:

Midwives Rules in verse (1939)

1. Every patient must be seen
2. Every midwife must be clean
3. Keep her tools and bag in order
4. Wash her hands and arms in water
5. Instruments be disinfected
6. Report infection when suspected
7. Stay beside her losing patient
8. Swab with care on four occasions
9. Examine only as directed

10. Nothing burn unless inspected
11. Clean the bloody mess away
12. Until the 10th day you must stay
13. Learn the normal rules of labour
14. Write the TPR on paper
15. Immediately the head is born
16. Bathe the eyes in lotion warm
17. If no movement baby wakes
18. Then at once resuscitate
19. If the baby's kind you guess
20. Tell the dad its going west
21. Never leave her on the shelf
22. Unless you do her in yourself
23. Administrations, Application notify in Registrations
24. So Rules 20, 19, 18 don't forget or you'll be slated
25. Rule 25 you must conform to Labour lying in at Home

(Written in 1939 and kindly donated by Chrissie Henderson, Stornoway, 2009; see Appendix 1 for original)

When health visitors were introduced into the community the role of the district nurses inevitably changed in most areas. Health visitors initially came from a variety of backgrounds and were not necessarily nurses. They visited poor homes and taught the public about hygiene as early as 1862. The first recorded paid health visitor was appointed in 1867 and was employed to assist the lady visitors, give advice and teach personal and household cleanliness. In the twenty-first century it is necessary to be a registered nurse or midwife and undertake a period of theoretical study in order to become a specialist public health nurse.

Topics in the health visitor's curriculum were: the management of the health of adults, women before and after confinement, and infants and children. By the end of the nineteenth century there were colleges offering training schemes. The five essentials in securing 'the health of houses' that Florence Nightingale taught and recorded in her 'Notes on Nursing' were pure air, pure water, efficient drainage, cleanliness and light, which would have been important to the training of health visitors. After the Maternity and Child Welfare Act in 1918 and Nurse Registration Act in 1919, the Board of Education laid down conditions for the appointment of health visitors, one being that the health visitor was a registered nurse. The Royal College of Nursing supported this requirement.

In the Outer Hebrides health visitors were not introduced until the 1970s. This caused problems under the NHS Qualification of Health Visitors Scotland Act (1974). All new nursing applicants involved in triple duty were required to have their health visitor certificate or gain an annual dispensation from the Secretary of State. As there was no guarantee that the application would be renewed every year there was uncertainty about the system. Factors, such as the difficulty of triple duty nurses travelling to the mainland to undertake the health visitor training, delayed the implementation of the 1974 Act in the Outer Hebrides.

A survey in 1984 revealed that there were nine health visitors in Lewis and Harris, and three in the Uist and Barra areas. In 1972 there were only three health visitors employed in the Outer Hebrides which explains why few nurses in this book had experience working with them.

The emergence of the health visitor in other areas however, caused concern to the Queen's Institute over the demarcation of boundaries. If district nurses were the main health professionals in the area who attended to 'all ages and stages' it is understandable that there was some controversy over the delineation of the district nurses' role and the duties of the health visitors. It was suggested that resentment was felt because the health visitor sometimes visited the patient while the midwife was in attendance. Resentment may also have been due to the health visitor receiving higher pay with shorter working hours than the nurse midwife, who could be working day and night.

CHAPTER TWO

District Nursing in the Outer Hebrides

Plane at Barra

A New Dawn

The nurses in this book have an extraordinary pedigree. They were part of a unique social experiment which saw a state-funded comprehensive health service introduced in the Highlands and Islands thirty-five years ahead of the NHS in the rest of Britain. They were highly trained – mostly as Queen's Nurses with solid grounding in the particular skills required for district nurses. Most were qualified midwives where training became mandatory and standardised after 1915. Most extraordinarily they inspired others, particularly in North America, to set up similar models of health care in remote and rural areas based around the nurse-midwife which had implications, in particular, for Kentucky.

In 1912 a committee was appointed under Sir John Dewar to consider 'how far the provision of medical attention in districts situated in the Highlands and Islands of Scotland is inadequate and advise the best method of securing a satisfactory medical service therein'. The reason behind this investigation into health care in remote areas was because self-employed crofters and fishermen were excluded from the benefits enjoyed by workers in the rest of Britain as a result of the National Health Insurance scheme in 1911. They received no wages and therefore could not pay into the scheme.

The Dewar Committee found appalling levels of care or even a complete absence of it in some areas of the Highlands and Islands: insufficient nurses, lack of organisation of nursing services, poor follow-up and treatment of disease, and mismanagement.

In the Outer Hebrides, untrained crofters' wives were attending each other at births and in the area of Barvas in Lewis, the doctor had reported the deaths of three mothers in twelve days. One of the committee maintained that this 'was the result of deficiency in trained midwifery skills'. Lord Lovat, a witness before the Dewar Committee, said, 'the medical salvation of the Highlands and Islands lies in organised nursing'.

By contrast, the secretary of the nursing association in Gigha, an inner Hebridean island which had a resident Queen's Nurse, reported the 'feeling of quiet security it brought to the inhabitants to have the nurse living in their community'.

There was concern at the lack of health education provision for the community. One medical member of the committee went as far as to say that 'a nurse in many cases is far more essential than a doctor'. The committee noted how overworked district nurses were, particularly district nurse Annie Maclean of Harris, in the Outer Hebrides.

Remarkably the Dewar Committee, after many months gathering evidence, managed to write its report in one day when it met at the North British Hotel in Edinburgh. Even more remarkably, the Treasury responded promptly, agreeing within a few months to provide an annual grant of £42,000 to fund a Highlands and Islands Medical Service (HIMS); the equivalent to one shilling and sixpence for each member of the population. The Dewar Report and its implications was seismic,

The Dewar Committee gathering evidence. (Highland Photographic Archive,
Inverness Museum & Art Gallery, High Life Highland)

reaching even to Kentucky, where the model of care was replicated with a view to protect and save children's lives (see Chapter Eleven).

The first objective of the scheme was to provide GP services for every member of the community. Doctors were also given financial assistance to buy their transport and housing. Funds were channelled through local district nursing associations to provide housing. Three houses for doctors and nine for nurses were completed before the advent of war in 1914.

A review of the HIMS was included in the Cathcart Report in 1936 which concluded that 'the Highlands and Islands were now attracting medical men of a quality superior to the bulk of practitioners who found their way to the Highlands before the service was instituted'. The report went on to claim that the combination of doctor and nurse was extraordinarily impressive: 'Many of the doctors said that practice in their areas would be impossible without the services of the nurses, and everywhere we were told that co-operation between the doctor and nurse leaves nothing to be desired.' Nurses' knowledge of patients assisted in early detection of illness and their work on health education was of particular value.

The Highlands and Islands had already been providing a successful, state-funded and affordable health service for thirty-five years before the NHS was established in 1948. The Secretary of State for Scotland introduced the NHS (Scotland) Bill in the House of Commons in 1946 by informing the House that the HIMS had provided the necessary pointers towards a comprehensive service for the whole country. In addition, the war years had witnessed a state-funded hospital building programme in Scotland on a scale unknown in Europe, which was incorporated into the new NHS.

It is said that the main change which occurred when the NHS was created in July 1948 was the way people could obtain and pay for medical care. Instead of paying fees they paid as taxpayers. For the first time hospitals, doctors, nurses, pharmacists, opticians and dentists were brought together under one umbrella organisation which was funded directly by the Ministry of Health and free for all at the point of delivery. District nursing services, including midwives and health visitors, became the responsibility of the local health authority under the control of the Medical Officer of Health.

Health education had been pursued during the war years but messages were now more concentrated on dangers in the home, infectious diseases and accident prevention. In 1951 the British Medical Association launched a magazine, 'Family Doctor', in order to promote health. Certain subjects were taboo however; contraception being one. Birth rates were rising and demand for beds outstripped supply, therefore domiciliary births rose. The main complaint from mothers was that there was lack of pain relief, as midwives in the community were not permitted to give the analgesic Pethidine until 1951. It had been approved by the Central Midwives Board (CMB) in 1948 and had been used in 75% of hospitals from 1948. Training for the administration of premixed nitrous oxide and oxygen anaesthetic was not taken up in many local authorities, as the equipment weighed twenty-two pounds, making it difficult for one person to carry. Additionally, the CMB rules stipulated that two midwives had to be present when 'gas and air' was administered and as many geographical areas only had one midwife, it was not worthwhile undertaking the training.

Where they Worked

The Hebrides are a group of islands off the north-west coast of Scotland. People have lived there for tens of thousands of years, surviving famine and storm, invasion and emigration and, in the modern era, discovery and romanticism by various luminaries like Mendelssohn and Boswell and Johnson. The archipelago comprises 119 islands, ten of which are now inhabited.

During the period from the 1940s to 1973, transport links between islands on the Outer Hebrides and to mainland Scotland were poor and many of the islands were not easily accessible. In some places roads were non-existent and communication was unreliable. This would have presented challenges to the district nurses. Major changes were also taking place at this time both socially and in the advancement of health care nationally which impacted on the delivery of nursing care.

The population of the islands was in decline throughout the twentieth century; the precariousness of island life being underlined in 1930 when St Kilda, the westernmost inhabited island group was evacuated due to illness, insufficient medical care and economic failure. This was highlighted again in 1938, just before the period covered here, when the Secretary of State for Scotland was asked in parliament if the islands of the Outer Hebrides were to be kept populated.

The decline continued during the Second World War. In April 1940 the distinguished travel writer H.V. Morton published an article entitled 'Islands of Sorrow', having discovered that the island of Lewis had lost twenty times as many of

Map of the Outer Hebrides in relation to the United Kingdom. (© Crown Copyright)

its sons per head of population in the war than any other part of Britain. Although other rural areas in Britain experienced a rise in population from 1960 onwards, this did not occur in the Western Isles.

Lack of employment opportunities prompted the establishment of the Highlands and Islands Development Board in 1965. The first regional development agency in Britain, it had wide financial powers to provide grants and loans. Fishing was also expanded and by 1971 there was a large fishing fleet based in the Outer Hebrides.

Yet young people still left the islands in droves. Further education centres were located in mainland Scotland and while pupils from rural Lewis could find secondary education in Stornoway, Harris, Uist and Barra pupils had to attend school in Skye, Inverness or Fort William. Consequently, these areas without senior secondary schools suffered from absentees in the fifteen to nineteen years age group in particular, this being the largest group of emigrants in the 1960s.

In this period it was common for most men to work as fishermen, crofters or weavers. A number of weavers are still scattered throughout the islands producing Harris Tweed, for which there is an international demand. Tourism is also a major means of employment. District nurses now often provide care for people of many nationalities, which was unheard of in the 1940s when Gaelic was the principal language of most islanders.

In 1940 traditional 'blackhouses' were still commonplace in the islands. The blackhouse usually had three apartments, two for the family and a third for the cattle. A few of the blackhouses were still being occupied in the early 1960s in the remote areas. A Dr Doig provided a vivid picture of a blackhouse when he came to Lewis in 1930, describing one house as being 'constructed by local material such as flat stones and driftwood or spars from old ships, and straw from oats or barley for thatching. The smoke got through the thatch, soot adhering to it and the roof was stripped to the cabers each year and used as manure on the croft'.

Typical blackhouses (Taigh Dubh in Gaelic). (© Alice Heywood)

Prior to the tuberculosis outbreak in the Western Isles in the 1930s, in which Dr Doig 'led the fight against the disease', a number of articles appeared in journals which claimed that the reason for the rarity of some diseases, including tuberculosis, occurring in people who lived in blackhouses, was that the peat smoke had 'valuable antiseptic and protective properties'. It was even reported that the Public Health Inspector had suggested that the burning of fires in the blackhouses, along with the sea air which came in through the open and ill-fitting doors, counteracted any poisons within the houses. Even the American nurse Mary Breckinridge, on her visit in 1924, wrote, 'I will say this for the blackhouses – they were the only warm ones I found in Great Britain.'

During the decades covered by this book however, most people lived in stone built houses, with the bigger homes being occupied by the minister and the doctor. District nurses in each area had a house in the village allocated to them for which they paid rent. Houses were also being built for district nurses in various geographical areas from the 1940s. Despite these developments, electricity and running water were not connected until the 1950s in many places in the Outer Hebrides.

Transport

The biggest change from 1940 onwards was the improvement in road links, removing the necessity of nurses having to take a boat. Benbecula was linked by bridge to South Uist in 1942, then by causeway to North Uist in 1960, while the Baleshare and Berneray causeways were completed in 1962 and 1999 respectively. The bridge connecting Lewis with Great Bernera was opened in 1953 and in 1997 the Scalpay Bridge connected that island to the rest of Harris and Lewis. It is possible now to travel the length of the Outer Hebrides, from the Butt of Lewis in the north, to Barra in the south, in just one day. Only fifty years ago, it would have taken several days. In the Uists especially the formation of bridges and causeways between islands has changed the way of life for the inhabitants who no longer have to rely on a ferry service.

Few bemoan the old days when a district nurse based on a small island depended on the ferry to transport patients to a larger island for transfer to hospital by road. In 1946 an ambulance was loaned from St Andrews Ambulance and the Red Cross to the Harris areas, on condition that a nurse always accompanied the patient in the vehicle. The expected time allowed for travel by ambulance from Tarbert in Harris to Stornoway was five hours and Leverburgh to Stornoway, nine hours.

New transport links have been the saviour of smaller islands but they came too late for Scarp, off the west coast of Harris, which in 1951 had a population of seventy-four. By 1968 the primary school and the Post office had closed. The island's infrastructure deteriorated and the population further decreased to twelve in 1971. The island subsequently became deserted as services could no longer be sustained.

Air links also opened up. Flights between Stornoway and Inverness started in 1934, while the first drive-on ferry commenced in 1960. The first time an aircraft was used for transporting a patient was in May 1933, as fisherman John McDermid was in urgent need of an abdominal operation but was much too ill for the long sea and road journey. He arrived at the Western Infirmary in Glasgow just over an hour after the aircraft had left Islay.

While Mr McDermid was still recovering in hospital Dr Alex MacLeod, from Uist, read of the event in a newspaper. He then persuaded the Daily Record to pay for a flight to bring one of his patients, the Rev Malcolm Gillies, who was terminally ill in Glasgow, back to his home in Uist, to spend his remaining days there. The flight took one hour and forty minutes from Glasgow, whereas the patient would have spent a day travelling by land and sea. The flight signalled the first air ambulance to the Outer Hebrides and demonstrated the scope of aerial evacuation from, as well as to, hospital. Until 1993 an air ambulance service based in Glasgow transported patients from the islands to mainland hospitals for specialist treatment.

In the twenty-first century the airports that serve the Outer Hebrides are in Stornoway, Benbecula and Barra, the latter being the only beach airport in the world to handle scheduled airline services.

Religion

There are few communities in the United Kingdom which have so closely integrated day-to-day life with religious belief as those of the Outer Hebrides. The people of Lewis, Harris and North Uist are mostly Protestants. There are at least seven churches in the town of Stornoway and often two in each of the villages in Lewis, Harris and North Uist. In South Uist and Barra the communities are predominately Roman Catholic.

The 'Stornoway Sabbath' as Sunday is known, is considered to be a day of rest. Only one shop is open in the town and that only for a limited time. This would not have been accepted or even considered in the period covered here, when there was strict adherence to the community's religious beliefs. However the first Sunday flights to Stornoway commenced in 2002 and in 2009 Calmac began a ferry service on Sundays, despite protests from religious groups who valued the island way of life.

The influence of religion in the Outer Hebrides, particularly in Lewis, cannot be underestimated, although the strict Sabbath observance was not confined to the Outer Hebrides. In a north Yorkshire fishing village in the 1970s a writer spoke of the many similarities this area had to Lewis, such as the strict sanctions on any kind of work on the Sabbath. The work of the district nurse was classed as necessary but caseloads were reduced on a Sunday and only essential tasks carried out. It is likely that the nurses were expected to attend church when work permitted.

Social Life

As in other aspects of island living, people's social lives have undergone a great deal of change. For example, following the introduction of television to the islands in 1971, there was a decrease in the number of people attending both the cinema in Stornoway, which had opened in 1934 and the mobile cinema which until then had provided an essential service in remote areas.

A study of Leisure and Society in Lewis published in 1975 reveals that young people had an established pattern of weekend activities. They began in the town area of Stornoway at a ceilidh (concert) and then the young people toured the country areas attending dances throughout the night. It was noted in the study that excessive drinking was a problem, although it was suggested it was not as extreme as amongst their predecessors. According to the report, the focus of spending among the 18–25 age group in the 1970s tended to be for the purchase of a car. The study goes on to suggest that there was a low level of interest in organised leisure pursuits, while middle aged and older women with cars spent time visiting friends.

Modern ease of travel has enabled the introduction of centres of academia in the islands, such as the nursing campus of the University of Stirling and the University of the Highlands and Islands, which in turn have led to greater cultural diversity. Residents in the Outer Hebrides in the twenty-first century have the opportunity to enjoy many aspects of culture and entertainment. Each locality throughout the islands has its own particular social calendar which can include summer shows, night classes, or activities pertaining to health. This is in sharp contrast to the period covered here, when transport or work commitments restricted socialising.

Health Services

Between the 1940s and 1970s most of the health care for the community of the Outer Hebrides was provided by the general practitioner (GP) and the district nurse. The GP generally ran his practice and had surgeries in his home. As medicine advanced, so did the nature of their work.

Back in the 1940s diphtheria was still rife and a rising level of tuberculosis led to one death every two hours in Scotland. The post-war baby boom certainly added to the district nurse's work – since nine out of ten babies were delivered at home. Smoking was also prevalent – by 1961 more than four out of ten women and six out of ten men were smokers.

In this period there was one district nurse attached to each geographical area of the islands, many with no doctor in residence, and only a small boat for transport. District nurses who worked in remote areas cared for all ages and stages of life and were on 'first call', making the decision about whether to call for medical assistance. The 'triple duty nurse' as she was called, carried out general nursing, midwifery and health visiting. In most remote areas in Scotland, this type of nurse was the norm. Most district nurses attended to all the health care needs and lived in the area they covered. They were indeed of the community, in the community and for each community they served.

In 1896 the Lewis Hospital opened in the town of Stornoway, with fifteen beds. The sanatorium (as the tuberculosis hospital was called), with twenty-five beds in 1920. The latter treated people with tuberculosis – many of the returning servicemen had TB. Uist had a small cottage hospital, as did Barra. People who required psychiatric services had to be transported to a mainland hospital for treatment.

The sanatorium remained open between the wars when TB was prevalent among the fishermen and fisher girls of the Outer Hebrides, who worked by following the herring shoals around the coast of Britain, returning home to spread the infection through entire families, often with fatal results. With the introduction of anti-tuberculosis drugs the incidence of TB decreased and the sanatorium was used to treat all infectious diseases until 1975, when it was redeveloped as a geriatric hospital.

The advent of the NHS in 1948 was supposed to herald the building of new health centres, where multidisciplinary teams provided a range of care, but they were a long time coming. The pattern of nursing in the community changed and the nurse and the GP shared the same practice population. In the Outer Hebrides change was even slower. The first health centre in Stornoway opened in 1977, some ten years after they were established in other parts of the country. Only one nurse who worked in the 1970s spoke of a team approach in community care. Similarly, the multidisciplinary team approach appears to have been slower to develop in the Outer Hebrides, with one nurse commenting that there was no psychiatric nurse until the late 1970s.

In 1974 a reorganisation of the NHS transformed district nursing. Teamwork in community care replaced the lone worker in many areas and care became less localised and possibly less rooted in the community. This change also moved district nurse management from local authorities to health boards.

District nursing has changed in recent years. District nursing teams now include community staff nurses and health care support workers. Stornoway now has a University Campus where nurses can carry out all their training locally with community health care theory and practice incorporated into the general training. Nurses have the choice to work in the community when they complete their training.

This is in contrast to the nurses in this book. After completing their general and midwifery training they were expected to carry out further training on the mainland as Queen's Nurses before being employed as a district nurse. The Queen's district nurse training was carried out at one of the Queen's Nursing Institute training centres situated throughout the UK. At that time student nurses, if they wished, could do part of their general training in the Lewis Hospital and the remainder in a Glasgow hospital. Most nurses opted to do all of their training in mainland hospitals. How nurses were trained was transformed in 1959, with the first university diploma in community nursing being introduced in Manchester. Once the training of district nurses moved into the higher educational institutions, the Queen's Nursing Institute Scotland (QNIS) discontinued training in 1968.

The implications of the many changes that took place through the three decades would impact on the lives of health professionals everywhere in Britain. Some district nurses in the Outer Hebrides were affected by the changes and whether these changes affected them differently from nurses in other areas is unknown.

CHAPTER THREE

Training

Loch Seaforth ferry

Travel

All the nurses in this book originated from the Outer Hebrides and remember travelling to their training hospital on the Scottish mainland. For some it was not only their first time away from home but also their first time on a plane, boat, train or bus. Many nurses commented on the trauma of leaving home to go to their training hospital. They described accounts of long and arduous journeys (the map on page 26 gives a sense of some of the distances involved).

Jean gave an account of her journey in 1952 from her home to Glasgow:

> The bus was at 2 o'clock from my home in Harris and I got to Stornoway about 7 in the evening and the *Loch Seaforth* was due to leave at midnight … It was January and lo and behold it was stormy and the *Loch Seaforth* couldn't sail. I had to phone the matron at the Victoria Hospital in Glasgow where I was going to let her know why I was delayed. I felt she must have thought I was living in the back of beyond somewhere – which I probably was! I had nowhere to stay in the town of Stornoway so then I had to go back home which was another five-hour journey. Luckily the boat sailed the next day.

It was a very stormy crossing and in those days in the *Loch Seaforth*, the luggage was on the deck and the sea was coming over it. I remember getting to the nurses' home, and I was the last one to arrive. That was awful, I felt terrible! Then when I opened my case, all the sea water had come through it, and all the text books that I had to read and all my clothes were ruined. When you were accepted for training you got a list of everything you had to have, grey cardigan, your shoes, and all the books you had to read. That was my start! I was sharing a room with a girl from Dundee and she had been to a pre-nursing school and of course I hadn't so that didn't help as I felt she knew much more than I did. I was so homesick and I couldn't sleep because of the tram cars going up the side of the hospital and down the other side of the road.

Despite her daunting experience Jean's tenacity was evident. She was not deterred even by the five-hour journey back to her home in Harris and the return again the next day. The time her journey took to return home from Stornoway is an indication of the remoteness of the area she lived in.

For Marion too, the experience of her journey to Glasgow in 1940 for her training remained with her forever. She had travelled thirty miles by bus from her home in the west side of Lewis to get the ferry and recalled:

Map showing the distance some of the nurses had to travel.
(By Cnbrb – Own work, CC BY-SA 3.0,
https://commons.wikimedia.org/w/index.php?curid=34131487)

The steamer, the *Lochness*, left Stornoway at 12 midnight and it was reeling. I wakened with a fright at the sound of bells ringing! Someone said that it was the cattle that had got loose and the noise was to waken up the crew to the problem. At that time there was always cattle on the boats. We then took the train from Mallaig and I smelled for the first time coal and oil. I wasn't used to the smells. When we got to Crianlarich, the train stopped for a short while, and when it started again it was going backwards and I was worried something was wrong. A lady on the train reassured me and told me that it was alright as the engine was on the other end.

All Marion's new experiences, the smells and the noise of the traffic, remained in her memory, such was the impact these encounters had on her.

Catherine from Uist was only sixteen when in 1941 she travelled with her aunt by plane to Glasgow to start work in a hospital as an auxiliary nurse. She was too young to start her training but wanted to work in a hospital until she was old enough:

It was my first time off the island and I went by plane. I was so disappointed because the first thing I saw on the tarmac at Renfrew Airport was a seagull and I felt so let down because I had been used to seeing so many of them at home.

Another nurse, Morag, had read about trains but had never experienced rail travel before she left home to start her nurse training in 1941:

I left on the ferry from Scalpay Pier in Harris at 9 in the morning and it was 7 o'clock the next morning before we arrived in Glasgow. We got the boat to Kyle of Lochalsh, a train to Inverness and then a train to Glasgow. I had never seen a train yet it felt very natural, I think reading about it, you sort of knew what they were like. I was sick on the ferry and I didn't like it. There were a lot of soldiers, sailors and airmen travelling. The trains were packed and it was good fun so the time passed very quickly. Of course it was war time.

A Glasgow tram 1950s. (© CSG CIC Glasgow Museums and Libraries Collection: The Mitchell Library, Special Collections)

27

One nurse, Katag, who in 1946 was travelling back to the island to take up her post as a district nurse in Ness, describes how the weather hampered her:

> When I left Glasgow I travelled by train to Mallaig. The boat could not berth at Mallaig due to the heavy seas so I had to stay the night at a hotel. The following day the boat was due to come in, but once again it couldn't get into the quay so I had to stay another night. Eventually we boarded the *Claymore* and arrived at Kyle to discover that that the Stornoway boat had left and I had to stay in Kyle. When I arrived in Stornoway the next day my brother met me and told me there was no buses that evening due to the snow and frost. However a bus did arrive and I managed to get home and stayed the night with my parents who lived in the district I was going to work in.

General Training

Lena from Uist remembered her training as being enjoyable despite 'the pay being poor and there was a lot of studying'. She was known as Lena although her full name was Malcolmina, Lachmina after her two brothers who had died of diphtheria. She always felt that her name was unusual and long. 'When I started my training I met another student, Mary Theresa Bridget Kathleen. I used to say to her, "Mary, I'm glad that your name is longer than mine". We got on well and stayed in touch after training'.

The general nurse training was much the same whichever hospital the nurses chose, although it could vary, as Jessie describes:

> In 1946 when we were accepted for our training we were sent our acceptance letter, instructions as to what to bring as well as regulations that stated that we had to be healthy and that the training would last four years. We were in PTS (Preliminary Training School) first and then we went to the wards. They signed you on then, like a contract for four years and then you got a month's holiday. You didn't get a holiday until then. We were up at 6.30am and in bed by 10pm. It was hard work and with a war being on we had people sign on for nurse training who wouldn't normally have. Titled people, the Queen Mother's niece was two classes ahead of me but they never finished their training. They just went back to their castles that had been used as hospitals. There were eighteen of us at the start and at the end of four years, nine finished. On each ward you went on placement you were given a report and if your work was not up to scratch you were sent to the Lady Superintendent. If you broke a thermometer you had to pay sixpence for another one. It was very hard and a lot of nurses dropped off with ill health. My father always said to me, "whatever you start you must finish" and I did.

A typical set of 'Instructions to Probationers on Entry' dictated what they were required to bring with them. Material and instructions for making their uniform dresses were included. The length of the uniform had to be 'nine inches off the ground'.

THE ROYAL INFIRMARY OF EDINBURGH.

INSTRUCTIONS TO PROBATIONERS ON ENTRY.

Probationers are required to bring the following things :-

At least 8 aprons uniform pattern.

A red cape, to be had from Messrs Turnbull & Wilson,
60 South Bridge, Edinburgh.   Price......................

2 linen bags not less than 27 inches in width—to pattern.

8 pairs half sleeves (for which the material is supplied).

8 belts.

12 collars.

A watch with a seconds hand.   (Wristlet watches are not
permitted).

Before entry, candidates will be supplied with material for two
dresses, which must be made according to regulations.

Underclothing should be of strong material.   All garments
must be clearly marked with surname in full.

3 underskirts of washing material (to be worn at all times
with uniform).

Boxes must be distinctly marked.   Full name to be painted
on at one end.

Only one small sized trunk in addition to a hat box or suit
case is allowed. If very large boxes are brought,
they cannot be stored, and must be sent home.

Instructions for probationer nurses from the Royal Infirmary Edinburgh 1940

Not all hospitals required their students to pay for their uniform. Some of the other hospitals operated under the 'corporation' and the nurses had free uniforms and more money than the voluntary hospitals. A fee of £5.50 had also to be paid in some hospitals before they could enter the training school and at the Royal Infirmary in Edinburgh candidates had to get their own uniforms made.

Candidates were not accepted for nurse training if they were under 5ft 2in. They had to be over nineteen and under thirty-one, which indicates how young these women were who worked alone, often in isolated areas, in the Outer Hebrides.

L.S. 33

ROYAL INFIRMARY,

EDINBURGH, 3, **23** - **1** - 19**40**

TRAINING SCHOOL FOR NURSES.

DEAR MADAM,

We have decided to accept your application, and shall be pleased to offer you a vacancy in the Preliminary Training School on

June 23 ᵘᵈ 1940

Please confirm your acceptance of this vacancy and give the address to which you wish your uniform sent.

Copies of regulations as to uniform, etc., and material for two uniform dresses, will be sent a month prior to entry.

The Fee for the Preliminary Training School (£5, 5/-) should be forwared at least 14 days before entry.*

You are required to be re-vaccinated, if this has not been done within two years.

Should any unforeseen circumstances arise to prevent you from accepting this vacancy, you are requested to notify me immediately.

I remain,

Yours truly,

E. J. Smaill

Lady Superintendent of Nurses.

MISS. ██████████████ *E. J. C.*

Cheques and Money Orders to be made payable to the Treasurer, and sent to the Lady Superintendent of Nurses.

290-M.9.31-7.36-10.38

Acceptance letter for Nurse Training at the Royal Infirmary Edinburgh 1940

An example 'Timetable for Nurses and Probationers' shows that probationers had to rise at 6.15am to be in the wards for 7.15am. They were then off duty at 8.30pm. It reveals the long hours the probationers worked and explains Jessie's description of the the work as being hard.

Jessie remembers that there was an early morning roll call in the dining room to make sure that everyone was up from bed. Then some nurses read a portion of the Bible and they all had to kneel and recite the Lord's Prayer. In the first year nurses recall carrying out mostly cleaning; dry and damp dusting of the ward they were assigned to. With only one and a half days off a month it is not surprising that Jessie mentions the high rate of attrition at the time. It would be reasonable to think that all the nurses who completed their training should be considered as survivors.

THE ROYAL INFIRMARY OF EDINBURGH.

TIME-TABLE FOR NURSES AND PROBATIONERS

L.S.-61.

I.—STAFF NURSES AND ASSISTANT DAY NURSES

RISE	BREAKFAST	WARDS	LUNCH	DINNER	TEA	RECREATION	OFF DUTY	SUPPER	BED
6.30 a.m.	7 a.m.	7.15 a.m.	9.10 or 9.35 a.m.	2 or 2.30 p.m. Sundays, 1.30 or 2 p.m	4.30, 5, or 5.30 p.m.	2.30 to 6 or from 6 p.m.	8.30 p.m.	8.35 p.m.	10 p.m. Lights out 10.30

One Day, and One Half-day off Duty each Month.

RISE	TEA	WARDS	OFF DUTY	DINNER	RECREATION	BED	Three Nights off Duty each Month
7.30 p.m.	8 p.m.	8.30 p.m.	8 a.m.	8.5 a.m.	8.40 to 11.30 a.m. or 4.30 to 8.30 p.m.	9 a.m. or 11.30 a.m.	

On Fridays and on alternate Sundays Night Nurses go to bed at 9 a.m. and may rise at 4 p.m.
Nurses wishing to Sleep out of Hospital for nights off, or on the night before a day off duty, receive permission on request.

III.—PROBATIONERS

RISE	BREAKFAST	WARDS	LUNCH	RECREATION	DINNER	TEA	OFF DUTY	SUPPER	BED
6.15 a.m.	6.45 a.m.	7.15 a.m.	9.10 or 9.35 a.m.	10 to 1 p.m. or 2.30 to 6 p.m.	2 or 2.30 p.m. Sundays, 1.30 or 2 p.m.	4.30, 5, or 5.30 p.m.	8.30 p.m.	8.35 p.m.	10 p.m. Lights out 10.30

One Day, and One Half-day off Duty each Month.

SUNDAY HOURS

10 to 1.30, or 2 to 10 p.m. alternately.   (Every fourth Sunday Nurses do not go on duty until 1.30 p.m.)

All times off Duty are subject to exigencies.

Punctual observance of the above Time-Tables is required, and permission for alteration of any of the hours, or absence from meals, may be had from the Lady Superintendent of Nurses.

Timetable for probationer nurses

Catherine was too young to start her general training and worked as an auxiliary nurse in a psychiatric hospital near Glasgow. She then went on to do her general training and her midwifery training in Glasgow before carrying out six months' tropical disease training in London. Her plan had been to go abroad to work but her sister, who had also been a nurse, died and her parents were so upset they did not want her to go. So she gave up the idea and carried out Queen's Nurse training in Glasgow. Catherine enjoyed her training and was 'more interested in midwifery that anything else'. Her training was carried out during the war years:

> … because the war was still on there were restrictions on the number of staff so it was a hard life, we had a hard working day, but we enjoyed it. I think we had a day off a week but that didn't come into consideration as we were happy doing what we were doing and nobody moaned about time off or money.

After her Queen's Nurse training in Glasgow she worked as a district nurse in Falkirk, before learning to drive and securing a post in Argyll, where she worked for three years. She decided to go to London to do private nursing as she felt 'she was getting rusty' and needed a change. By the time Catherine came to be a district nurse in the Outer Hebrides it is clear she was very well qualified and experienced, in common with many of her colleagues.

Marion remembers an incident which occurred while she was carrying out her midwifery training in Glasgow:

> The war had started – and there were blackouts and all the lights went out. We carried a torch but you had to keep it under your fist so it couldn't be seen. There were trams and they did not have destination indication light on them during the blackout and the conductor had to stand on the step and shout what its destination was. This day I was coming back from my day's work and got on the tram. Of course we were wearing corporation uniform, green, and when I came on the conductor said, "you staun there and shout Auchenshuggle! I've been shouting it all day". So I just stood there and at every stop I was shouting "Auchenshuggle!" in my best Lewis/Glasgow accent – because that was where the tram was going! We didn't have to pay a fare, we had tokens because we were working for the corporation, so there I was shouting "Auchenshuggle" at every stop. And do you know it is a Gaelic word – it means the 'field of rye'. I never forgot my trip on the Glasgow tram!

Trainee nurses were often initiated with practical jokes by the patients or colleagues. Jean was no exception. While in their initial three months preliminary training probationers went to the wards on a Sunday:

> My first Sunday on, I was sent to a male ward and I was absolutely shattered because it was a male ward and I didn't know what to expect! I was put into what we called the slunge [sluice]. Honestly I was in there and I was so nervous I didn't want to come out! I had to clean the bedpans and I could see my face in them – they were chrome, not like nowadays. So I thought I had better come out. The men knew I was new on the ward. This man shouted "I want a bedpan," and back I went, got the bedpan, did everything I was asked to do, put the screen round him, put the bedpan down, did everything in the proper manner and then he shouted, "I'm ready nurse," and do you know what was in the bedpan … a doll! One of the ward maids then said, "Do you know what happens when you have a baby?" I was totally innocent of those things at the time and they were trying to frighten me! The patient was laughing so much at all this that I was terrified he was going to have a heart attack. Imagine, the whole ward knew about my first experience! He was a nice man. I got to know his wife and children when they came in but I never forgot my first day on the ward.

Donalda's first ward placement was on the 'septic ward', where she had to have a 'hard skin' to cope. She recalled:

> There were a lot of men from the shipyards with big carbuncles on the back of their necks because their jackets were rubbing on them all the time. It was a male ward. The Glasgow men had quite a sense of humour and every time when they saw me coming into the ward they used to say, "Here she comes, the wee highland teuchter!" I was small in stature.

She recalled the fun she had during her training, such as the practical joke that was played on her:

> It was April Fool's Day and I didn't know, and one of the senior nurses asked me to go to the kitchen for a long stand. I trotted along to the kitchen and this big woman asked what I wanted and when I told her I had come for a long stand her reply was, "Well you can just stand there for a while." Many a student nurse was caught out with that joke over the years!

Donalda also remembered her initial introduction to nursing in Glasgow in 1945 when she was eighteen years old:

> When I arrived in Glasgow we were looking out of the taxi window and we could see the lights and the tram rails. The lights had come on after the war and it was really amazing to me. I had applied to the Western Infirmary and I had also got my call up papers at the time, but when I filled them in I said that I had applied for nursing to the Western Infirmary and I had been accepted, so I didn't hear any more about the call up. I didn't want to hear anyway. An aunt in Glasgow took me to the Western Infirmary for an entrance exam. It wasn't very difficult at all. I had been two years in the Nicolson Institute Secondary School in Stornoway. I went to the preliminary training school and waited for the result and this big woman with ginger hair, in uniform, came, and she told my aunt that she could go. And then she turned to me and said, "Come along nurse," and I looked to see where the nurse was and it was me she meant! So that was it – three months in the preliminary training school, but at the weekends we were in the wards.

It was difficult for the students to make ends meet and Donalda remembers that she had to buy her textbooks but that her pay was so little that she often borrowed money from her aunt who lived near the hospital: 'We had to wear black stockings and twice I was sent to matron's office because I had a ladder in my stockings. I used to get the stocking seconds in the Barrows'.

When Donalda finished her training she went off to London to work in a private nursing home which had midwifery care on one side and geriatric care on the other. She thoroughly enjoyed her stint there but started looking for another job as 'the pay was so bad, although by this time I was paid every week and it was getting better.' She applied for a job in Newfoundland which at that stage had established a cottage hospital system largely modelled on the Highlands and Islands Medical Service.

She was interviewed in London, accepted for the post and set off on a two year contract in 1952. She took a plane to Newfoundland from London. It was October and she had a journey of two days and two nights on a ferry: 'It stayed in the outer ports during the night and sailed during the day into all the small ports, delivering cargo and people.'

When Donalda arrived at Harbour Breton, a small community on the south coast of Newfoundland, she had hoped someone from the hospital would meet her as she had a trunk with 'all her worldly goods, which wasn't much'. She was disappointed however:

There was no one meeting me and I walked up and the snow was very deep and I couldn't see the road. They only had electricity in the hospital. There were no street lights but the snow was bright enough, but I was in the ditch half the time with the snow over my knees.

Once there, Donalda found she wasn't alone:

There were just two of us, the other nurse, I can't remember her name, she was from Newfoundland and just above the hospital there was the doctor's house and she phoned him and he came down. He came down and he asked me where I came from. I said Stornoway, "Oh did you know a Norman Mackenzie?" I said yes, plenty of them! He was in the Navy with a man with the same name but the island of Lewis is quite big and I didn't know who he was talking about.

Donalda at the cottage hospital in Newfoundland

Donalda shovelling her way into the hospital

In my spare time, which wasn't much, I went for walks around. The summers were lovely and the hill up from the hospital had a lovely view. The hospital carried out quite a few operations there, even caesarean sections if necessary.

I remember one night a lady had a caesarean section and had a haemorrhage. We did have a list of people that we could call for blood transfusions if we needed them, but this was in the middle of the night and she was 0 negative. I said, "I'm 0 negative," so they took a pint straight from me into the woman. I was lying on a bed beside her while she was getting my blood. I was feeling fine afterwards but the doctor ordered me to bed. At first I refused but he made me.

At that time too during the operations we nurses carried out the anaesthetics. There was an anaesthetic trolley with oxygen and ether on it and there was a mask and a gauze swab and you just poured a few drops of anaesthetic on the swab and took the tube from the oxygen cylinder under the mask and that was the anaesthetic. There was one nurse doing the anaesthetic while another one of us helped the doctor on the other side of the table during the operation. There were a lot of appendectomies at the time, while the major surgery was transferred to St John's General Hospital and a sea plane would come for the patient as the ferries would take too long. One time when we were doing an appendectomy the doctor asked me to, "Come over to this side of the table and you will do the operation and I will help you." I did the incision and he was on the other side and we went right through, and I remember I parted the fibres and went down and he said, "See if you can find the appendix." It wasn't acute, it was chronic appendix. So I put my hand in and I think he did too and showed me: "Right, now clamp it." It was quite a long one. "That's right, that's it, sew up now," which I did. I said "Don't tell the man it was me that did his operation," but the staff told him and before he left hospital he gave me a silver dollar which I still have. We certainly got lots of experience!

Improvisation learned in Canada would later stand Donalda in good stead. On her return to Britain, she did her Queen's Nurse training in Glasgow before taking up her post in the Outer Hebrides.

CB

Notwithstanding the hard work in the wards, the long hours, the teasing of the nurse by the patients, the practical jokes and the lack of money, the Hebridean women persevered and completed their training. They were geographically mobile as most of them moved from their general training school to a different nursing school, often in a different town, to carry out midwifery and then moved again to complete their district training. Some even went further afield to gain experience and training. It's no wonder one nurse commented that 'when we were on district we were prepared for anything'.

The accounts of these young women from the Outer Hebrides suggest that it may have been difficult for some of them to adapt to the new culture of big cities. Despite

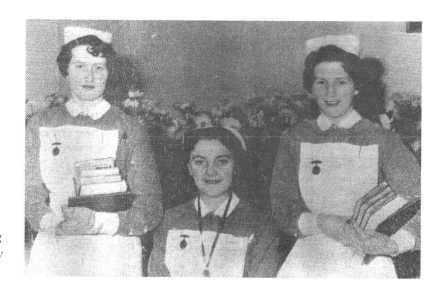

Lewis Prizewinning Nurses. (Stornoway Gazette)

the challenges they all appear to have accepted the encounters that their journey presented. They really were resilient women, who had the ability to spring back after an episode of difficulty. When they got to their training hospital they needed stamina to cope.

Most of the women left their island home to undertake often four to five years training in mainland hospitals. General nurse training usually took three to four years, midwifery one year and the Queen's Nurse training four months. Some women undertook further specialist courses in nursing sick children, tropical diseases and mental health nursing, so that by the time they took up posts in the Outer Hebrides they were extremely well qualified.

From the 1940s onwards there was concern about the future and duration of the Queen's Nurse training. In the 1940s to mid-1950s The Lancet included articles about both. The training course in 1948 involved a six-month residential course but was later reduced, depending on the qualifications of the nurse. By 1960 it became four months. Topics covered in the Queen's training included sociology, public health, nutrition, dietetics, psychology, hygiene, house planning, sanitation and tuberculosis. The scope of health issues incorporated in the examinations indicates the wide range of knowledge that was expected of the nurse at that time.

Queen's Nurse Badge.
(© Peter Maleczek)

It was prestigious to be a Queen's Nurse and nurses were very proud of their Queen's Nurse training. Neillag defines why: 'We were always told in Queen's that because of our training you could go to the desert and manage!' Another nurse went so far as to receive a level of preferential treatment because she was a Queen's Nurse. Morag recalls:

> I took very ill in Clydebank where I was on district and I was three months in the Glasgow Western Hospital. If you were a Queen's Nurse, you were the 'Bee's Knees'. I was treated as a private patient in the corner of the ward. I remember discussing my pay with the ward sister and mine was even better than hers. I remember telling her it was seventeen pounds and something, and that was in the 1940s.

At that time the more qualifications a nurse had, the greater her pay. Thus district nurses with their added qualifications were often on a higher salary than their colleagues working in hospital. According to a 1947 account record in the Northern Regional Health Board, which included the Outer Hebrides, only one nurse received a monthly salary of £17, while other salaries were considerably lower, although there was no indication of their qualifications. The record specifies they were all trained nurses, which might imply that one had an extra qualification.

Nursing is often said to 'run in the family'. It may be that many nurses were encouraged to take up the profession by their predecessors, however it is unknown how many Queen's Nurses were related.

A Hebridean Queen's Nurse in the 1930s. This picture shows the mother of the nurse shown on page 38 who worked in the 1960s.

A Hebridean Queen's Nurse in the 1960s

Jean describes the difference between the professional practices of a Queen's and a non-Queen's Nurse:

> It would have been in the early 1970s and I had to demonstrate in front of a whole crowd of nurses how to do a wound dressing '*à la* Queens'. Everything had to be as clean as possible. When you went in to a patient's home, you folded your coat; put it on a chair with paper underneath it to keep it clean. We gave them good antenatal care and then went back again for the delivery but they knew the Queen's Nurses. The mothers were always told what baby clothes they had to buy. We wanted everything done in a proper manner! There were other nurses too, not Queen's. We were different. When I was doing my Queen's in Glasgow some mothers would notify us when they went into labour, and we would get a call in the middle of the night to go to a woman's house and often when I would get there they would have nothing for the baby or the delivery. We had not been attending them but they still wanted us to deliver them. We Queen's Nurses always kept a close eye on our midwifery cases and always checked mothers had clothes for the baby.

Jean's experience of mothers notifying the Queen's Nurses instead of their own midwife when they went into labour appears to have taken place in the 1950s on the mainland.

The probable surgical dressing technique which the nurse was demonstrating is included in the booklet 'The QNI District Nursing Techniques Handbook', which maintains that instruction should always be 'clear, concise and comprehensive taking nothing for granted and leaving nothing to chance'.

Such was the demand for Queen's Nurses in the late 1940s that there was a waiting list to carry out the training. It would be reasonable to suggest that the reason may have been due to the reduction of nurses in training during the war years, which was commented on in QNI's Annual Report of 1944: 'The number of district nurses applying for training has been disappointing. Had it not been for the number of nurses who have re-joined district work as well as the married nurses who have continued in the service, the shortage of district nurses would have been serious'. Some academics believed that the national shortage of nurses threatened the government's plans for the National Health Service, which was implemented in 1948. Subsequently, in the period from 1939 to 1949, a series of reports and investigations into nursing were carried out.

In an attempt to address the shortage of nurses in the Outer Hebrides during the period from 1940 to 1944 it is recorded in the Lewis Nursing Service Sub-Committee (LNSSC) minutes that the procedures for the appointment of district nurses were changed. At that time the LNSSC provided the local nursing association with the names of prospective district nurse candidates and the association would choose someone they thought was suitable for their area. Because of the shortage of nurses, the LNSSC agreed that in some cases they would appoint the nurse directly 'in case the nurse might accept another appointment before the next meeting of the Association'. Clearly they were pre-empting any chance of the nurse being appointed elsewhere.

Most of the nurses carried out their Queen's training in Castle Terrace in Edinburgh but Nora recalled that she was unable to do so:

> I applied to Edinburgh to do my Queen's district nursing and came home.
> One of my sisters took ill and was taken to hospital and that delayed the
> date that I was given for my Queen's training in Edinburgh. I was then asked
> if I would I go to Ayr as they didn't have enough places for students (in
> Edinburgh). I didn't mind. I didn't know where Ayr was! I knew Edinburgh,
> that was why I wanted Edinburgh but I decided I wanted to get through my
> district training so I decided to go to Ayr and that was in November 1952 to
> March 1953, six months. I did enjoy Ayr and I was surprised.

Queen's Nurses were trained in various places in Scotland, mostly in Edinburgh but also in Aberdeen, Glasgow and Dundee as well as Ayr.

The 1944 minutes of the LNSSC indicate that most nurses who applied for posts were Queen's Nurse trained. One applicant was not Queen's trained and there was controversy over the proposed appointment. She was appointed but in most instances the minutes of the LNSSC reveal that if there was a Queen's Nurse and a non-Queen's Nurse applying for a post the outcome was the appointment of the Queen's Nurse. Marion, the nurse appointed in this case recalles the reason why she was appointed over the Queen's Nurse: 'The other applicant had been working abroad as a missionary and did not have much experience of the island, whereas I had been working as a relief district nurse in the area'.

By the 1950s it would appear that in the Outer Hebrides there was a shortage of trained district nurses. Mary remembers that after she was appointed as a district nurse in 1955, she and three other nurses 'were shipped off to Aberdeen to carry out a Queen's district nursing course'. After gaining district nurse posts without Queen's Nurse training, in some cases, the local health board seconded the nurses from their posts as Isobel explained: 'I got married in 1958 and I stopped working, but I did a lot of relief, then in 1966 I got a district so I felt that I had to do district training and went to Edinburgh. The local authority sent me'. Ann was reluctant to carry out her training: 'The reason I did Queen's was, when I applied for the district I was told I would have to do my Queen's training, otherwise I probably wouldn't have done it.'

The local authority would have paid the Queen's Institute of District Nursing (QIDN) for the nurse's training at a cost of approximately £90. In addition, travel costs would have been needed and payment for relief staff. It seems likely that the expenditure was incurred to address the shortage of trained nurses in the community.

During their training Queen's Nurses were given ten driving lessons. In their minutes of 1953 the QIDN reported that the driving of two nurses in particular was so unsatisfactory that further lessons were recommended and if they were still not ready for their test they should continue their driving lessons in the area to which they were appointed. Kate suggests that nurses were bonded by their training, including their driving lessons:

> We got our driving lessons in Edinburgh – it was included in our training. I sat my test in Greenock and I got through the first time. I went on contract then to Greenock. I thought the driving instructor was testing me when he pointed along the road and said, "There goes Dr Campbell." I didn't look and said that I didn't know any of the doctors as I had not been in the area for long. "Oh," said he, "You are very snappy Miss Macleod." I thought he was going to fail me!

Although Kate (centre, back row) married she obviously went back to work as she went on to receive her long service medal

After training we all had to carry out a year's contract in a district or else you had to pay £30 which you didn't have as a salary then. I'm glad I did it and I wouldn't give it up until I finished it all [training]. I would never think of getting married … as you weren't allowed to work if you were married. I stopped working in 1953 because I intended to get married.

A similar concern about paying for training if it was not completed was highlighted in the minutes of a Queen's nursing finance committee meeting in 1953. Arising from the minutes was a request that a 'penalty of £35 be imposed on a nurse for failure to complete her period of service under contract in respect of district nurse training'. The matter was being taken up with the woman's solicitor.

Christina recalled an interesting story while she was carrying out her Queen's training:

I was working in a very nice area of Edinburgh and had to visit a lady who had suffered a stroke. I had an awful time finding the house and had to go upstairs to a flat in a yard where the woman lived. Her two daughters-in-law were there. The old woman was only wearing a dirty vest and one of the women asked me what I needed. They then brought into the room lots of new night dresses, bed jackets and vests. I thought this was strange – all these new clothes and the patient looked so dirty. The daughters-in-law said the patient had plenty of clothes but she was so mean she wouldn't 'put clothes on her back' and never let them into the other room.

They then took me into the other room and it was full of all sorts of things like blankets, sheets, tea sets, dinner sets, silver tea services, jewellery and lots of other stuff. They even gave me a couple of things that were of no value although I had great doubts about taking them. When I got back to Castle Terrace I excitedly told the other nurses about the room that was like Aladdin's cave. The next day I was not on duty and I asked the nurse who was at the patient in the evening, "What did you see?" "I saw nothing," said the nurse, "Just a big empty room." I could hardly believe it. But sure enough the next day when I went to the patient, the room was completely empty, and the daughters-in-law … were very cool towards me. One of them said they had spent a whole night taking all the stuff away – they didn't say where it came from or where it went. I was very disappointed as I had never seen so much stuff in my life apart from in the shops. My conclusion was that the old woman must have been a receiver of stolen goods and probably her daughters-in-law knew nothing about it as they had never been allowed into the room before her illness. The other nurses teased me that it was all a dream, especially as the other nurse the next day saw nothing. If it was a dream I told them that I had received stolen goods! I felt very guilty about the necklace and earrings I had been given and every time I saw a policeman in Edinburgh after that I wondered if he was coming after me. I thought my career had ended before it had begun!

CHAPTER FOUR

Image and Lifestyle

Social Life

Very few nurses in the period appeared to have outside interests apart from attending church. There was however a difference between the cultures of the islands; on Lewis, nurses did not appear to have any social life, while their counterparts in Uist enjoyed various activities. Nevertheless, it was evident that religion played an important role in many of the nurses' lives. The Outer Hebrides was known at the time for its religious values, therefore it is unsurprising that most of the nurses were part of this culture. One nurse, who complained about not having time off to attend church, did not stay long on the island, illustrating the importance of their faith.

Often a nurse's faith and work were intertwined, as Morag relates: 'I was dedicated to my work, I lived for my patients and my nursing and I was never one for dancing, going to concerts or anything like that. I was quite happy to work. I felt the work was from the Lord'. Isobel was thankful when her working life was over: 'I took off my uniform when I retired and went down on my knees and thanked the Lord. I dealt with an awful lot of things. Something could have gone wrong but thank the Lord it was uneventful.'

Catherine, who had worked for thirty years in a remote area and was responsible for schools, health visiting, midwifery, and general nursing, felt differently:

> I think I was so confident. I can't say that I always depended on my faith. You always tried to do what was right whatever faith you were working with. I may have asked if I was doing the right thing but that was it. But I was very happy. It was a lovely time. Socially we were looked up to in the village, the policeman, the headmaster, the postman, the minister and the nurse were all in the same category. We used to get invited out to a lot of things. I used to play a lot of badminton and you had the occasional wedding you went to and they also had a post office club that we went to and we played table tennis and badminton there. If you wanted to go further afield we went over to Carinish to dances and debates. When the causeway linking North Uist with Benbecula was opened in 1960 there was a big dance and I had the honour of being judged the Causeway Queen which just goes to show the lack of talent! At that time, we had a telephone exchange and when I went out I told the man in charge where I was going if any calls came for me, he let them know where to find me.

Uniform

Uniforms have been part of the nurse's image since the Victorian times when some uniforms were reminiscent of the parlour maid dresses with stiff white aprons and starched white collars. By the 1940s the traditional uniform was a symbol of nursing's traditional authority and social standing. The nurses all took pride in wearing their uniform, especially those who were Queen's trained. Part of their assessment during training was concerned with their appearance in uniform. Cathie describes her uniform:

> Navy blue dress and a coat, something like your baseball cap nowadays, with a skip hat. It was warm, but it rained so much in the area I worked in that nothing protected me. I was brought up in a place where there were lots of hills and valleys for shelter. When I came to this area the only shelter I could find was beside a house.

Mary remembers the hat she wore: 'You could have your own style of hat. I had quite a nice one, but you had to wear the bonnet with the brooch if you were a Queen's. The hat I had was the kind that we still wear in Church, flattish one with a brim. It was like a pudding bowl, more or less'.

The uniforms the nurses wore were probably cumbersome in the summer, and the hat created problems in the wind, but most of the nurses persevered and always wore their full uniform. Nurses reported how the Hebridean weather affected the wearing of their uniform. Rebecca had problems with her hat: 'Half the time in the winter your hat wouldn't stay on!' Catriona was practical and sensible about how she wore her uniform: 'If it was windy and wet and cold, we just dressed in wellingtons and trousers, because if you had wellingtons on you couldn't see the trousers. I always wore my hat'. Catriona was required to go on horseback to a nearby island, which was part of her practice area, so it would certainly be more suitable to wear trousers than a dress even though trousers were not part of the uniform at the time. Hats were a problem to keep on in the windy weather, but nurses felt they were not in complete uniform without them. Maryann says: 'I never went out without a hat. I was always dressed in full uniform. Being on my own district meant a lot when you were in uniform'.

Most nurses maintain that they were proud of their uniform. In 1958 it was suggested that if nurses did not have a

A Hebridean Queen's Nurse in her uniform in the 1940s

hospital uniform pride would be lost and the competitive spirit that prevailed between nursing hospitals at that time would be discouraged. It was also maintained that it gave the wearer authority, self-confidence and a sense of discipline. However, that view was dismissed by others who contended that uniforms displayed 'the fragmented historical identity of a profession driven by issues of class and status'. It is possible that district nurses, whose uniform was part of their identity, depended on it to symbolise the status they appeared to have within the community. Nurses who prefer the current uniform of 'scrubs' may indicate that they want to discard their historical image. In the twenty-first century a national uniform has been introduced but it is unknown as yet whether it will influence the image of nursing.

Nurses speak about their fondness for the uniform, including the hospital badge. It was important to most of them, as Nora recalls: 'I can't remember being off sick when training but if you missed time through sickness you had to make it up before you could claim your hospital badge. The hospital badge was very important to show off pinned to your apron. Every hospital had their distinctive badge.' Jessie felt very strongly about what her badge, the Pelican, signified. She believed that the service supported the patient too much at the expense of the nurse:

> The patients always came first, that's what our badge stood for and we were reminded of it every day and that was wrong! It was a picture of a pelican bird. You only got the badge after four years. Only nine out of my class of eighteen in got it. The pelican takes blood out of its own breast to feed its own! Priority was always given to the patient, always the patient, and that's all very well but the nurse's welfare was also important! The pendulum has swung too far now. It was too far the other way back then but it's too far the other way now!

A Queen's Nurse with her car in the 1950s
in Ness near the Butt of Lewis.
(Comunn Eachdraidh Nis)

The Pelican badge

The Pelican badge was chosen by the Royal Infirmary training hospital to represent the charity and self-sacrifice of nurses, pelicans being known to feed their young from their own blood. Nurses trained in the hospital are referred to as 'Pelicans'.

Nurses in the Outer Hebrides at the time considered that wearing the uniform was important and they regarded it as a significant part of their training. It helped them to appear professional, which they had been taught was important in order to give the public a good impression of them. Some patients saw the nurse's uniform as proof of her competence and therefore found it reassuring.

The Nurse's Bag

Nurses also identified the bag they carried as part of their uniform. The contents of the bag, usually a Gladstone, has been described as 'part of the imagery of district nursing; a container of secret powers and instruments of healing'. Contents of the midwifery bag (which was a separate bag) were itemised in most maternity textbooks. Christina was annoyed with the contents of her 'general' bag:

> I had this black bag and there was nothing in it but forceps and a syringe! There was no throw away syringes then, you boiled them. I went to the Nursing Officer and asked her for some bandages and cotton wool and things for my bag because if I met for example an accident, I had nothing in the bag. I was going around with that bag and anyone would think that there were an awful lot of wonders in it. She said, "Oh no, you can't have that, but I will give you some lint," and she would give you lint until the cows come home. What I was going to do with it, I don't know! She didn't give me a bandage, even a triangular bandage if somebody had hurt themselves, or cotton wool to clean a wound, no, not a thing. It was just because that was what was done in those days. Then years later when I became a Nursing Officer, I made sure that there was a cupboard full of supplies and the nurses were given whatever they needed, gloves and everything that was necessary for their work. That was one thing that I saw to.

The nurse's bag was part of her uniform, as Morag explains:

> I always carried my bag. I never found it heavy. When the doctor came to do his visits on the island I went with him and we walked. There was no road then, not for a vehicle anyway and I carried the doctor's case for him too, because he was older. I didn't carry my own when he was there. I only carried my own for confinements.

The midwifery bag for confinements would have been heavy, especially if the nurse had to walk a distance, as Rhoda who worked in the 1940s states: 'It was very heavy, but we were young and we were so keen. We had gas and air with us for maternity cases and that was heavy.' Very few nurses complained about this or any part of their work however, despite the challenges of their working environment.

Many nurses in the 1940s and 1950s rode a bicycle, which must have been difficult to balance a bag on. Maryann found she could manage: 'I could set it on the bike, some way or other; I didn't have it on my shoulder like they would have now.'

Similarly, those nurses who had to go in a small boat to the smaller islands such as Scarp, over difficult terrain and sometimes against the winter elements, would have needed the strength to carry the maternity bag and perhaps another one with gas and air. There were occasions when patients' relatives carried the nurse's bag for them, particularly during the night. Relatives usually had to fetch the nurse from her house and accompany her to attend the patient. Rhoda recalls a night when she had just returned from a confinement and there was a man waiting at her cottage door:

> He said indignantly, "I have been waiting for you." I replied that I can't be everywhere. He then said, "Give me your bag, my wife told me not to wait a minute talking." I asked, "What you are going to do with my bag?" He said, "You'll be lighter when you start running, you run and I will carry your bag." So he did and we were on time for me to deliver the baby.

Nurses' bags have been transformed over the years, with lightweight canvas shoulder bags replacing the familiar Gladstone bags of the twentieth century. For these nurses, the contents of the bag were described as being inadequate for their practice. Conversely, present day nurses are able to carry emergency drugs, adrenaline for instance, in case they encounter a patient with anaphylactic shock. Most items are now disposable, in stark contrast to the equipment of the past, when nurses had to boil glass syringes and sterilise dressings in the patient's oven.

A twentieth-century Hebridean Queen's Nurse managing her bag and her bike. (Comunn Eachdraidh Nis)

Equipment

The lack of equipment in the period is evident as nurses complained of being short of supplies. Any equipment necessary for patients would be stored in the nurse's cottage. Nurses indicated that although they didn't have much equipment they kept a supply of cod liver oil and orange juice for distributing to mothers. Rhoda remembers that mothers were coming for orange juice and cod liver oil every other day, such was the demand.

Mary recalls sterilising cotton wool balls when she was carrying out her training in Edinburgh:

> We were putting the dressings and cotton wool in the oven in the milk tins, we did not have the 'dressing packs', they started by about 1967. I remember rolling cotton wool balls to sterilise them. We put them in the patient's oven. You also made some swabs and things like sanitary pads for the patients, and the doctor invariably thought the sanitary pad was a mask for his nose.

A description of how to sterilise dressings is included in the Queen's Nursing Technique Book 1954–1957, which states: 'dressings are baked for one hour in a moderately hot oven. Dressings will be a golden cream colour if properly baked'. This 'sterilisation procedure' would have been a time consuming task but the nurse was also reminded in the textbook that: 'Much time can be saved by planning to employ waiting time. Time spent in talking and listening to the patient is not wasted'.

Nurses described being practical and making use of what was available at the time. Although electricity came to many places in the islands in the late 1950s it took some time before all areas were connected to the grid. Likewise, running water gradually became available and in some places outside wells were still functioning into the 1960s. Mary describes how she managed patients who were incontinent:

> I could get quite good rubber sheeting, which you could borrow from the nursing service and I probably kept a couple. I then got worn sheets that you could tear down, and I would always have big long washing lines outside the house for the sheets. It was amazing how the people just coped. Mind you, you learned as you went by. I remember asking a young mother how she coped and she said, "I just do the tops and the bottoms of the sheets and the necks of the things." We had of course bedpans and bottles. There was a room in the cottage that was really like a surgery where we kept the various bits and pieces we had.

The 'bits and pieces' described by the previous nurse are explained further by Chrissie:

> There were no commodes, but there were bedpans. People were kept in bed a lot more then. The doctor would put people to bed if they had a bad cold or if old people had flu, they would have to go to bed. We did have mackintoshes and draw sheets and old sheets. That was all really. There were no pads.

Neilina recalls the equipment that was available to her in attending to her patients:

> We kept rubber sheeting and that sort of thing. After the war people didn't have all that much, like linen, so you were forever getting old sheets from somebody and keeping these for draw sheets. It was hard work, because incontinence pads hadn't come into force then and even to keep their skin [intact] meant that we had to visit incontinent patients often.

The importance of keeping their patients' skin intact was regarded as a matter of professional pride and Neilina maintained that 'even if the patient died you took pride that the skin was whole'. Such was the pride the nurses took in their care of the patients.

Christine reflects on the difficulty of not having a sphygmomanometer (blood pressure monitor) on one occasion when she attended a home confinement and complications arose:

> After the delivery, the baby was fine and the mother seemed fine; the doctor had just gone downstairs and was going to his car when the mother had a fit, so fortunately he was there. Her blood pressure must have shot up. In those days we didn't have a sphygmomanometer, we just had to rely on her going to the doctor. That was the 1960s and we didn't have a blood pressure machine. In later years it was routine to take a patient's blood pressure after she had a baby.

It was the responsibility of the nurses who worked in remote areas to go to the town area to collect equipment. As Mairi recalls, they accepted that this duty was carried out in their own time: 'We just had to phone to get our dressings and things from Stornoway. We would go over maybe on our half day and get them.' It would seem that a nurse's life was her work and collecting equipment in her spare time was just another accepted part of it. For nurses working in or near the town area it was easier to access resources as Dolina explains: 'You had the daily visit bag, with dressings or whatever you needed. We were quite well stocked; we had no problem with stock'.

Gaelic Language

In the middle decades of the twentieth century the majority of people in the Outer Hebrides spoke Gaelic. Earlier in the century the Dewar Report stated 'that a good knowledge of Gaelic was preferable for nurses working in Gaelic speaking districts'. The nurses however had different attitudes towards Gaelic. Mary describes her experience with the language: 'I had been born in the west side of Lewis in Barvas, so I knew Gaelic, but not to speak fluently, because I only took it when I went to school in Stornoway. But my word I had to learn it because there was a lot of Gaelic spoken in those days!'

It is understandable that patients would prefer to communicate in what was effectively their first language. Although a large number of people spoke Gaelic Catriona did not perceive it a problem if a nurse did not speak it: 'The patients all spoke English, but some, especially the older ones, preferred speaking Gaelic.

Nurses would have managed fine if they couldn't speak the language because people in every house spoke English'.

In contrast, Jean had a patient who only spoke Gaelic and was visited by a doctor:

> I remember a relief doctor came. He wanted to learn Gaelic and he thought it was going to be dead easy! I had a lady who could only speak Gaelic so I said to him, how about giving her a visit. I told the old lady there was a new doctor coming and he wanted to learn Gaelic. So off he went. I didn't see him afterwards. I called on the patient the next day and asked her how the doctor got on with his Gaelic. She said, "He was bad enough when he was talking in English but he was ten times worse when he was talking in Gaelic!"

Catriona practised in Uist, where only 73% of the population spoke Gaelic in 1971, compared to rural areas in Lewis where 90% spoke the language. It was also reported at that time that 30% of the population in some rural areas of Lewis could speak only Gaelic.

Morag, who worked in the 1950s when English was not commonly spoken in the islands, recalls an incident when an obstetric difficulty arose:

> There were twins delivered and there was a retained placenta. They sent the husband for the doctor and he asked the nurse, "What will I say to the doctor?" He was told to say, "*Fhuair sinn a chlann ach cha d'fhuair shin ach a chlann.*" (We got the children but we got nothing but the children).

The nurse appears to have been using the Gaelic to relay a message to the doctor without alarming the husband. If she had said that the placenta had not been delivered it would possibly have caused him worry, which the nurse was trying to prevent.

The culture of the islands and of the nurses at the time was in contrast to twenty-first century health care, where openness is the norm. The incident conformed to the nurses' training at a time when they were instructed to care for relatives as 'failure to extend this consideration and care may cause anxiety and suffering for the patient'. By conveying her message in Gaelic that the babies were born, but that there were still problems, this nurse prevented anxiety for the patient and relative.

Gaelic was the first language of most of the nurses and many did their Queen's training in Edinburgh. In a study of district nurses working in the mainland of Scotland one nurse recalled, "I was carrying out Queen's training in Castle Terrace in Edinburgh and I heard this language going on … it was Gaelic. There were a lot of Highland girls and they were talking in Gaelic". It is not surprising that these women spoke their own language when they met, as it was part of their culture and natural to communicate in their mother tongue.

From the comments of the nurses here it would seem that there was no disadvantage for a nurse who worked in the Outer Hebrides and did not speak Gaelic, yet it appears that it was very helpful to have a working knowledge of the language.

Marriage

Many Queen's Nurses expressed disappointment that they had to leave work after they had married. Most of the district nurses were highly qualified, yet some of them only worked for a short period. However, until the mid-1960s, many of them did return to work, as married women were asked to provide relief cover due to a nursing shortage. All of the nurses who worked in the earlier time period of this book were unmarried, but by the late 1960s many district nurses in the Outer Hebrides were married. Dolina recalls a colleague who had refused to resign when she got married which was obviously unusual: 'The nurse for the Point district was married but she just refused to resign, and she just kept on until she retired. It was a jolly bad thing that you had to leave your job because you were married'. Marion also explains: 'Before you got married you gave three months' notice as a husband was not allowed to live in the cottage'. Mairi got married in 1957 and left work because 'everyone left when they got married'. Undoubtedly, most nurses would have liked to continue working after they married.

According to the minutes of the LNSSC in the 1940s some nurses were allowed to carry on working during the war because others had to go to the services. When the war was over many married district nurses then had to resign. In the minutes of a rural district nurse committee in 1954 a discussion took place between the members about the appointment of married nurses. The conclusion they came to was that single nurses should be appointed but 'where a married nurse is better qualified she should be appointed if her domestic situation did not make the appointment inadvisable'.

By the 1960s debate continued as to how to resolve the national nursing shortage. The formal or informal 'marriage bar' which applied to public bodies and some private firms before 1939 had to be relaxed during the war and was not reinstated because of post-war labour shortage. Ann describes how the position for married women reversed: 'A couple of years after I got married it all changed. They couldn't get nurses so they had to take married nurses then, and it was good because young people weren't going in for district nursing at that time.' Jessie recalls that sometimes married women were allowed to carry out relief work in the 1950s: 'When I was relieving on the district, sometimes it was for three months at a time. I was a married woman. There were no full time married women on the district at that time but eventually they had a few married women working'. Chris remembers being allowed to have her husband stay with her in 1964 after she was married.

Despite the general shortage of nurses one doctor, writing in 1966, was not in support of married women working. He questioned whether the married nurse would be financially better off working, whether it was morally right for her to leave her children, whether she would be able to attend a refresher course on her return and whether she would be accepted by her younger colleagues. His rhetorical reply to each of his own questions was 'probably not'. Fortunately however, the Equal Pay Act of 1970 and the Sex Discrimination Act of 1975 assisted in changing behaviour and attitudes towards women in employment. Married nurses could no longer be discriminated against following the 1975 legislation.

Chrissie H and her husband make a very striking couple in their uniforms when they married in Stornoway

During the war nurses often got married in their uniform, particularly if they were marrying a serviceman, as money was scarce. Chrissie H comments that 'she knew she could not work on the district after she was married'. Some nurses married in uniform during the war years as they could not afford a dress.

Attitude to Work

Nurses on the whole did not complain about the work that they carried out. Christina recalls:

> We were happy enough to get on with our work and nobody bothered us. We had a nursing superintendent come out once or twice a year and she went with you to see the patients and checked your cottage to see that everything was in order, but that was all. It was really quite a happy job, I really quite liked it.

Rhoda shares this sentiment: 'I was very keen on my work all the time until I had to leave it. I loved going round the patients'. Nora maintains that her work gave satisfaction: 'There was satisfaction that is the word I want, satisfaction, especially when you saw somebody that was ill making a recovery'.

Regardless of whether a nurse worked in a rural area, a town, or an island with no doctor, they enjoyed their work. Dolina believes that they did not have the same concerns as the nurses of today:

> We weren't bothered about litigation or anything, which you have to be so careful about now. But you had to be careful what you said and where you said it, because there were always houses where you had to watch what you did, but they weren't the norm. There was no fear of litigation but things have changed and people have got to know more about their rights.

Maryann remembers 'How daring I was, I never had any fear going out in the middle of the night in the dark on my own but if it were now I wouldn't go. I just didn't feel any fear. Oh I was happy; I was very happy. I was on district nearly eleven years. It was my job and I was quite happy in it'.

Catherine recalls: 'It was a fulfilling time, because I learned a lot and I loved my work, I enjoyed it and every day was new and it was lovely. I don't really think I disliked any of it. I liked it all'. Isobel too reminisces, 'You just got used to it. Living in a rural area, you just worked and slept. It was your life'. Cathie too maintains that 'she enjoyed every minute of her working life … my daughter comes home from work complaining of being tired and fed up and I say to her "I never complained, I enjoyed every minute of my working life"'.

Most nurses at the time seemed to be accepting of their life and work balance. However, a theme identified in a 2008 American study which examined letters from nurses from 1900 to 2005, was of self-sacrifice versus self-care. Achieving a balance between caring for patients and caring for oneself was reflected in many of the letters.

Although the Hebridean nurses worked day and night at times most of them did not complain about their working time. Whether it was their faith that sustained them, the culture at the time or their evident love of their work is unknown. Apart from Rebecca who did not enjoy working on an island without a doctor and Jessie who expressed some discontent about her pelican hospital badge and what it symbolised, there are no other examples of nurses who were not happy with the lifestyle they had. Cathie summed up her life as a district nurse: 'I loved every minute of it!'

CHAPTER FIVE

Working Conditions

Housing

The minutes of the Lewis Nursing Service Sub-Committee (LNSSC) record that between 1933 and 1947 discussions often took place regarding nurses' accommodation. Although each geographical area had their own district nursing association all decisions made locally in the island of Lewis were required to be confirmed by the larger committee that met every two months in the main town of Stornoway.

The type of housing was varied, and depended upon the time frame in which the nurse was in post. In the earlier period of the 1940s the LNSSC noted that 'repairs to the nurse's cottage were an on-going agenda topic for discussion'. In 1933 repairs were needed for nurses' homes in Harris where the windows were 'requiring hinges and the cottage and surroundings were damp'. A later request for the 'installation of a sanitary convenience' was agreed, providing the nurses paid an increase in their rent.

At a Harris committee meeting in 1946, ranges in the nurses' cottages were described as being in a 'hopeless condition' and this was to be brought to the attention of the county council. At the same meeting it was stated that, 'in view of the numerous complaints from the nurses regarding the state of their cottages, a survey should be carried out, with a view to the necessary repairs to being carried out, as little attention had been given to the houses referred to during the war years'.

The condition of houses allocated to district nurses differed from area to area as Neilina explains: 'All we had were bare necessities! I thought it was terrible. When I came to the district in 1956 there wasn't a flush toilet inside the house. There was a deep well outside the cottage, and you had to put a pail on a string and get water'. Rhoda too, remembers she had complaints:

> The cottage was just awful. The stove in the living room wasn't working, the oven was broken and I had to do with a wee primus stove and no electricity, so I had Tilley (paraffin) lamps. But the state of the cottage was making me awfully unhappy, and if I did complain the answer I would get was, "Well they are going to build a new cottage." But when! There was no time specified. So I was there carrying on in the old cottage and it was very uncomfortable. Life was hard for the nurses and their surroundings did not help.

Electricity came to the islands in the 1950s but outlying areas were supplied later than towns. Most of the island of Harris was connected to the electrical supply in 1954. Toilet facilities in some of the nurses' houses were worse than primitive as Neilina mentions: 'In the first house I went to, there was a bath and a sink in the kitchen and it was really a disgrace, there was no toilet. It was an outside toilet, a dry toilet. It was terrible'. Two other nurses had made similar complaints to the Queen's nursing supervisor about the conditions of their houses. Rhoda made sure that others knew about the conditions that she had to endure in the west of the island of Lewis:

> Our Queen's nursing supervisor came once a year to see that everything was in order, but I was always emphasising to her, "How can you expect the district nurse to go out and teach hygiene when she can't have it in her own cottage?" It was an Elsan that we had (a dry inside toilet), and a big bath in the kitchen, with two big taps but no water. What the bath was for to this day I don't know! Someone local said to me it would do fine for dipping the sheep. Apart from having no running water, no electricity to heat the water, even if we got some, it wouldn't be an option to use the bath with people constantly at the door.

In the LNSSC minutes there is frequent input from a Miss Weir, described as the Inspectress of the Queen's Institute of District Nursing. In 1942 she informed the committee that repairs which were supposed to have been carried out some five years previously had not been completed. The response from the committee was that any complaints of this nature would be lodged in the proper quarter as soon as they were received. Miss Weir then suggested to the committee that because the repairs had not been carried out, the rents for the nurses' cottages should therefore be reduced to £10 per year, which the committee agreed upon. It is not clear how much rent nurses were paying at the time. Their salary is noted as being £185 per annum in the 1940s, and had remained unchanged since 1934.

The minutes portray Miss Weir as a formidable woman, whose priority was the welfare of patients and nurses. She certainly acted as an important advocate for nurses. The committee consisted of six to seven men, but her influence on nursing matters during the 1940s was evident. It was likely that Miss Weir had received many complaints from nurses such as Mairi who recalls:

> It was shocking. A woman came round once to see the houses and she said the nurses away from here had much better houses, she was disgusted. You see there was no electricity and it was a coal or peat fire we had. Sometimes when I would come home, after a day's work, I would try to light a fire but before I started there would be another call.

Basic facilities were lacking in many houses – no running water, inside toilet, or means to cook. Most nurses had open fires that had to be lit and kept stoked with coal or peat, making this a chore of necessity when they returned home from work. Some were luckier. Morag in Scalpay, Harris, recounts: 'I had a nice cottage down by the bridge, it was lovely. It had a bathroom, sitting room, bedroom and a kitchen'.

Joan, who worked on an island with no doctor, recalls an unusual problem she had and how the solution came through the kindness of the community:

> I had been asked to collect curtains for the cottage as there were none on the windows. I remember going into town and going to the shop to collect them and I was shocked when they just gave me the material. I thought what am I going to do with this material? And who came into the shop at the time but a well-known domestic science teacher and she offered to make them for me. What a relief as I didn't know where I would start!

Nora described her house in Harris as very remote. When she looked out of the window she could only see the top of another house in the distance. As well as being lonely and feeling isolated at times she describes another problem she had in her house: 'I had rats to keep me company and I phoned home and my father told me: "If you have a stick just give it a rattle on the wall and they will soon go away." I soon got used to it. The house had been empty for a few months and it was since then the rats had appeared.' Nora was also unnerved by the severe winds which blew on her home – frightening at first, especially being on her own, but she got used to that too.

In the 1950s an article in the Queen's nursing magazine described how a house should be built for a district nurse:

> The house should be soundly built with a view to economy of maintenance. The appearance should be neat and unpretentious and particular care should be taken to make the house fit in with its surroundings. The aim must always be to visualise the arduous life of the District Nurse with its long and irregular hours, and provide a dwelling which will make housework as light and pleasant as possible.

This ideal home would remain a distant dream for most district nurses in the Outer Hebrides!

In addition to their work, nurses' other chores would include finding fuel, water and lighting. Before they set out for a day's work, nurses in the 1940s and 1950s recall lighting a lamp for light, boiling water after they had fetched it from a well, and making food on a fire or range that had to be fuelled with peat or coal. Furthermore, many walked to see their patients. As well as adapting and coping with sub-standard accommodation, nurses also found themselves delivering care in patients' homes that were also of a poor standard.

Patients' Homes

In the 1950s, the housing situation in Scotland was worse than in England, with over a million people 'denied a reasonable home life through having to endure overcrowding, squalor and lack of sanitation'. The Outer Hebrides would have had similar problems. It is recorded in the Harris District Council minute book that housing was frequently on the agenda from 1952 to 1972 and that a housing programme was under way in 1961. It is likely that comparable programmes were in place in other areas of the Outer Hebrides.

Until the advent of mains electricity and running water in the 1950s nurses' preparations for some tasks invariably took longer. In some houses even boiling water meant first going out to fetch it from the well.

The traditional blackhouses in the Outer Hebrides were a challenge for nurses when they had to deal with resident animals and the patients. Rhoda remembers an animal providing a welcome distraction:

> I was called out to a young girl. She was running around at that stage, maybe two or three years old, and she fell into a pan of hot soup. They had taken the pan off the fire, and placed it on the floor as they usually did, and the wee one was running around and she fell into it. She burnt the whole of her back and word came for me to call. The wee girl did not want anyone near her or to touch her and when I saw the condition that she was in I understood why. It was a blackhouse and the family had a young calf which was in part of the house, as they were in those days. The young girl cried for the calf. She wanted the calf! Her grandfather said, "Right, we'll take up the calf," and that is how I managed to dress her wounds. By her patting the calf as I was dressing her burn at the same time, it took her attention away from what she was suffering. She was really badly burnt, but she healed up through time, but I was going there every day for a while and was very glad of the input from the calf.

By the 1960s nearly all the blackhouses in the islands had disappeared and housing had improved. Nevertheless, the blackhouses made an impact on the nurses who had to care for patients living in them. Marion recalls:

> The animals stayed in the building. The blackhouses were built so that the animals were separate from where the humans were staying and the animals

A traditional peat fire in the middle of the room. (© Crown Copyright HES)

were in what they called the kitchen. The next room was where the people sat and ate and lived. Now the next compartment again was the sleeping quarters. There were usually three beds and all the occupant's possessions were in their beds. At that time women who had a baby weren't allowed to walk for ten days, so I just lifted them out of bed and carried them to a chest on the other side of the room.

These nurses certainly had to use their initiative and their strength.

Mary Breckinridge, a nurse who came to the UK from America in 1924 and whose connection with the Outer Hebrides is discussed later, commended the blackhouse, despite its unusual accommodation. She maintained they were 'the warmest houses in Britain'.

Nurses seemed to accept their working conditions. When they compared their patients' homes on the islands to other areas they had worked in, it was generally noted by them that there was little obvious poverty in the islands. The islanders were in many ways self-sufficient, with their own peat for fuel, and food was easily accessible by fishing or agriculture.

Morag compares her home island to the poverty she saw during the war years when she worked in Clydebank. It suffered some of the worst bombing anywhere during the war and 4000 homes were destroyed:

> I was in Clydebank after the blitz, and there were just single end houses there and no street lighting or anything, so coming to Scalpay was like going to Buckingham Palace compared to what I experienced in Clydebank, with patients supplying towels and basins and everything that you needed. They were maybe not as modern as they are now, but there was always plenty of peat fires and I couldn't say that they were short of anything. They were quite well off. There was good fishing in those days and it was quite a prosperous island in my day. I don't think there was sanitation then or the water... no it was a good while after that that the water went round the Island. We had to go to the wells, but otherwise it was quite easy. In Clydebank, you couldn't get babies' clothes or anything, it was so poor, and a tragedy with 500 killed in the one night there with the bombing.

The self-reliance of people on the islands meant that their relative definition of poverty was different from other parts of the UK, where there would inevitably be a higher minimum standard. Nevertheless, there were other challenges for nurses as they carried out their everyday work, particularly in the long, dark, winter months. Cathie mentions that it was very dark and gloomy and that she always carried a torch. Marion, who also worked around the same time in the 1940s and 1950s, says that she too always had her torch but batteries were scarce and she couldn't even store them up as they would wear out. According to Mary there were Tilley paraffin lamps in every house and sometimes nurses had to borrow paraffin from a neighbour if the patient had run out, but most houses had bright peat fires so that helped with both heat and light. Often the sick person was in a bed near a fire; even in the kitchen. Mairi started her district nursing in the west side of Lewis in 1952 and she was delighted when electricity and running water were supplied the following year. It made life so much easier for her and her patients. When recalling her days working with no electricity, Ann says that despite going out in the dark at night, and in all kinds of weather during the winter months, at no time did she feel afraid as she had a job to do.

These nurses were fearless and prepared for any eventuality. They recounted challenges in their working lives, with many homes inadequately equipped to carry out care such as a confinement. Mary recalls her caring approach to her patients:

> When there was waste after a baby was born we knew to pack things up and take them home and burn them in our own fire. You had to be merciful, one person looking after kids coming home from school and all that goes with it. The mother might not manage to get things burned in the fire. There were often animals around but I was good at chasing them out. Rats were the only thing in the city, but definitely not here.

Mary clearly had no idea that a colleague in Harris had to deal with the problem of rats.

The discomforts of the nurses' own accommodation and the challenges presented by that of some of their patients do not appear to have deterred nurses from carrying out their duties. Another area of life which presented problems was the mode of transport they used; or in some cases, the lack of transport.

Transport

Car ownership grew rapidly in the post-war years. In 1963 a car factory was opened in Linwood, Renfrewshire. It was intended to reach an output of 150,000 cars a year, to meet the demand. Nurses working in the Outer Hebrides were likely to have been later in accessing cars than their counterparts on the mainland. Even transporting cars to the islands would have been difficult, involving a five-hour drive from a mainland city like Glasgow, then a ferry crossing. Nevertheless, it was reported that one nurse in the Outer Hebrides had a car in 1937.

Nurses walked or used bicycles, motorcycles and cars to carry out their duties in the 1930s and 1940s, as was noted in the minutes of the LNSSC. One nurse in Bernera had bought her own motorcycle in 1942 and an application was submitted from her to receive an allowance for it.

Some nurses never learned to drive. Marion describes her mode of transport as 'my two feet'. Some nurses had access to a car but couldn't drive. Marion's husband at times drove her around her visits but she did so much walking that in the area she was known as Barbara Moore, who was a well-known walker in the 1950s and 1960s. Rebecca in Harris didn't pass her test until 1975 and had to rely on a hire car for nearly ten years if she was travelling a distance to see her patients, both day and night.

Chrissie hadn't passed her test when she went on district but she still drove and depended on the goodwill of the police at the time. She says the local policeman knew she was driving without a licence and even sent her a message: 'I know you haven't a driving licence but you will be alright at long as you keep out of my way'. When Chrissie did sit her test and passed it was a relief that she didn't have to keep a look out for the police.

District nurses were vital members of the community and may have been trusted by the police who turned a 'blind eye' to the nurse without a driving licence. Nurses indicated that they were aware of the responsibility of using a car belonging to their employing authority. In most areas the nurse who had a County or later a Health Board car was not allowed to give lifts to people or take the car out of their own geographical area.

Nurses had to make their own judgements, even if it meant breaking the rules. Neilina describes getting a call to out to a pregnant woman who was visiting the island. She had started bleeding and seeing the urgency of the situation Neilina, after phoning the hospital to inform them, decided that she would transport the woman in her own car to hospital: 'You weren't supposed to use your car but if they had said anything to me I was ready to respond as it was the best option rather than dicing with the patient's life'.

Effie, a non-driver, also did not hesitate to improvise and used the transport available when she diagnosed a woman who was in labour with a breech baby: 'I thought she had to go to hospital. The poor woman was in labour and I went with her and we had to go over twenty miles in a rattly bus but we got there and everything turned out ok'.

Nora recalls her experience when learning to ride a bike:

> I never rode a bicycle until I went to Ayr to carry out Queens's training. I had to learn because buses weren't taking you out to your own district and it was a too far to walk from where the nurses' home was. I was trying my hardest; the people got to know me down on the sea-front in Ayr. The policemen in

Nurse in Bernera on her motorbike with a member of the community.
(Bernera Historical Society)

Ayr got to know me too because I couldn't do a right hand signal. They made me come off my bike if I didn't do that right hand signal. You see at that time there were no bikes in Scalpay where I came from, there were no roads and there were no cars. That is what people have got to remember.

Ceatag too had never been on a bike when she went on district and said that she walked everywhere until she acquired a bike:

The young lads in the village started to teach me to ride the bike. It was March, when the manure was being carted to the crofts. One of the lads stood at one end of the croft and the other was directing me sometimes straight into the pile of manure! They were all highly amused! When I eventually took the bike to the main road I had to cycle down a steep brae. The man helping me was shouting, "Keep the brakes on, keep the brakes on, don't let them off or you'll fall." I managed and after that I cycled on my own. Those were happy days!

Catriona on the island of Uist was adaptable when it came to travelling to her patients, who were located in the small islands which were part of her geographical district. She describes the thrill of getting her first car:

My first car was a Ford Anglia, that had to be started by cranking the handle, and then when I got the very first Mini that came to the island it caused a lot of excitement, people seeing a new car. I got that in my second year of work (1961). I also had to ride a horse, because of covering for the nurse in the next district's day off.

One of her areas was the island of Baleshare that could only be reached by boat or by walking a long distance across the sand:

I used to ride on a horse because it was easier than walking. I had a pony at home so I knew how to ride. We also had to learn to ride a bicycle and not be sea-sick in a boat; you had to be a seasoned mariner! I used to row myself across to the island in a boat and then collect a bicycle at the Post Office and just rode around, and it was a man's bicycle too. We wore dresses, and hats but we coped. We would have a saddle on the horse so that it was quite easy to get onto. It was a huge big horse and I had my bags. I also had a wee corgi, Terry, that went with me and he used to walk beside me.

Catriona provides a vivid picture of the nurse on her big horse, wearing a dress, riding side saddle, her bag in hand and her dog running along beside her. This mirrors the experience of the nurse midwives in the Frontier Nursing Service in Kentucky, modelled on the Highlands and Islands Medical Service, where the ability to ride a horse was essential. This was truly an age of multi- modal travel.

Catriona worked in Uist, where the culture may have been different from the islands of Lewis and Harris as I have not found any evidence that nurses on any of the other islands used horses. These photographs of Dr Alex Macleod on horseback in Uist indicates that horses were used as one means of transport on specific islands.

Some nurses, whose remit included small islands, were fortunate enough to have a man who organised the boat trip for them and rowed them across to the islands. Anna, who worked in Harris, including Scarp (an island off Harris which by 1971 was uninhabited), as part of her geographical responsibility, recalls her journeys there: 'I went over to Scarp on a wee boat, because there is no harbour, they had to draw up the boats on the shingle. They just had small boats.'

Nora describes her mode of transport when she was called to a patient who lived in a lighthouse:

> I knew that there was a family living in the lighthouse, but I didn't know at that time that she was expecting a baby. I got a call, and I left home quite confident, because I had been a number of times out at the lighthouse. It was a foggy misty morning and you can usually get the car out so far. There is a beacon light and then you have to leave the car there and walk the rest. I got my bag and was quite confident that I knew the road well. But being so misty I missed the telegraph poles which you always followed and I soon discovered that I wasn't on the right track and I was a bit frightened.
>
> I knew that it was a southerly wind that had been blowing as my husband had said to me when I left, "Don't think of calling a boat out to the lighthouse, because a boat won't land there because of the wind." When I stood still, I thought, the southerly wind should be in my face going out but it wasn't. I had the sense to know that I wasn't on the right track. So I turned back to the car and got a hold of the telegraph poles and followed them. When I got to the lighthouse the patient was over three months pregnant and bleeding quite a bit.
>
> I phoned the doctor and told him that the moor was very, boggy. No way could I arrange a stretcher to take her the three miles to an ambulance to the end of the road. He said, "The only other way to get her to hospital is by

Dr Macleod, Uist, on horseback

helicopter." The doctor came down and ordered a helicopter and it meant that I was away from home from the back of eight o'clock until after three in the afternoon. I couldn't leave the patient. It took time to organise the helicopter and arrange the hospital. The doctor then said, "You have got to accompany the patient." There was no escort on the helicopter at that time who could be responsible. I went in the helicopter and it was horrible. What a noise! But we got to the hospital safely. The doctor had arranged with the Health Board in Stornoway, that I would get transport at the hospital to take me back home.

It would have taken Nora two hours to get home.

Not only were the nurses adaptable to all transport situations, during the war years they were independent. They had to rely on their own skill to repair and maintain their transport as Maryann describes:

I always had a torch. A small one for my pocket and a big one in the car too – especially for the punctures you got in those days. They couldn't buy tyres in those days. In the war years I could change my wheel; I could mend my puncture and put the wheel back on. I did it umpteen times. I could do everything, and I had to. There was no one about and the men were all away [at war]. There were only women in the houses apart from the men on leave and they left a maternity case every time – in other words a lady who was pregnant!

The LNSSC minutes show that in 1944 there were only three nurses' cars on the island of Lewis; in Back, Gravir and Leurbost. In May 1947, the minutes report that a car had been delivered to the Bragar area, which was part of Shawbost nurse Rhoda's remit. She recalls that she was very excited when she got her car and that she was tempted to take it the twenty-five miles into town; however she always had to make sure that there were no births imminent or very ill patients.

The local nursing association had paid £90 towards the cost of the car and the Department of Health paid the remaining sum of £215. Also in the minutes was a request for a replacement car for the nurse in the Lochs area as 'it was over ten years old and in a very bad state'. There is confirmation in the 1937 minutes of the LNSSC that a Ford 8 car had been delivered for the district nurse in Lochs area. The nurse applied for a week's leave to learn to drive, as 'she is unable to spare time for driving lessons while on duty'. The committee agreed to the request. It is interesting to note that in 1937 there was a nurse who had a car, yet in the 1950s some nurses did not or could not drive.

Nurses overcame great challenges in their personal and working environments and the transport available to them had an effect on their practice. The weather, however, posed even great challenges.

Impact of the Weather

The Hebrides are known for their weather, with rain and wind which can often exceed 100 miles an hour and last sometimes an average of twelve hours a day. However, the sea is warmed by the North Atlantic drift, giving the islands milder winters than those of the mainland. Mary Breckinridge, who visited the islands in 1924, commented on the weather: 'The winds were so terrible that bicycles were almost useless and the nurses had to walk miles over the moors to reach their patients'.

Nora in Scalpay, Harris recalls:

> Gales … that was another thing! In an easterly wind the ferry couldn't move out. If there was a real howling gale, you would be dreading getting aboard a ferry or boat. Sometimes, they just couldn't move. The weather had a tremendous impact on our work here, especially gales and ice and snow.

Effie remembers an evening when the weather was so wet and windy that by the time she arrived at the patient's house she had to remove her wet clothes and borrow some from the woman in the house. The snow and ice affected the nurse's ability to travel to patients as Cathie remembers: 'You could hardly stand on the roads they were so icy, never mind drive a car. I would leave the car at home and walk as it was safer'.

Catherine had a close shave once when she was driving during the night on a call out in a very remote area on the mainland. She recalls that she: 'Reversed the car and because it was frosty the car came to rest on the edge of the river and I couldn't get the car to go forward. It kept going back all the time. I decided my life was not going to end there and I just put the foot down hard on the accelerator and managed to get out and going. It did slow me down a bit.

Most of the nurses said that they were adaptable and determined to reach their patients. They indicated that they would never refuse to go to a patient, regardless of the availability of transport or severity of the weather. Katie from Uist was affected after a particularly harrowing journey. A birth crisis arose at the Uisinish lighthouse in Uist during stormy weather. There were two ways to reach the lighthouse; either by five miles across a rarely used track over the hill or by open boat. The lighthouse keepers naturally chose the boat as the only option. Katie was terrified during the very rough crossing, so much so that she would not go on an open boat again and 'even the MacBraynes ferry was viewed with mistrust'. Katie did not refuse to attend the patient in the lighthouse however and her uncle stated that 'the journey was worthwhile as there was a new healthy baby at the lighthouse.' It is interesting that the same nurse who was so terrified of the stormy weather safely delivered undiagnosed triplets at a patient's home in 1950.

The triplets Katie delivered are presented to the Queen on her visit to Uist in 1953

Anna remembers sometimes having to stay for long periods in patients' homes and overnight because of inclement weather:

> I stayed sometimes for a night and a day too. You couldn't get out if the weather was bad. I remember the first January I was in district in Harris, I had a friend who had come down to stay with me and I was called to Scarp. I was there all night and she went away. What could you do? You had to stay until the weather got better.

The weather had an element of control over the nurses' lives. Ceatag describes using an opportunity in terrible weather to continue to provide a service for their patients during a severe snow storm in 1954:

> The snow was so deep in places I wore wellingtons, oilskins and carried a walking stick. Men from the various villages I visited would take my arm and help me along from one house to the next. There were no snowploughs in those days. Some young men employed at the sugar factories were on their way home on leave at that time and they had got stuck in the snow. They phoned the cottage to tell me they intended walking home to Ness [twenty-six miles away]. I took my opportunity and asked them to call at the doctors on their way so they could collect some penicillin, codeine, and other medicines for me before my stock would run out. The boys dutifully brought me a large sack containing everything I required.

Jean had a similar experience to Nora in the previous section, finding it quite frightening when she had to depend on telegraph poles to locate the same lighthouse:

> I had never been to the lighthouse and it was away out in the middle of nowhere, so when I got to the end of the road where I had to park the car I stopped to put on my wellingtons. A couple who were working at potatoes came over to me and said, "Don't go on the moor just now, it's much too misty and you will get lost. Come back in the afternoon and when you come back follow the telegraph poles and that will take you to the lighthouse." I came back later and the couple were waiting for me and said, "You're safe enough now and can carry on." Off I went with my case, following the telegraph poles and I could hardly see a thing in front of me – not a sheep and certainly not a lighthouse. I kept thinking I am on the wrong track but I got to a dip in the road and was so relieved to see the lighthouse.

Later, in the 1950s, Isobel remembers the snow preventing her from reaching her patient and having to enlist her husband's help: 'The weather was so bad I had to get my husband to row me across the loch to a maternity case. It was a fishing village and people used boats for their livelihood so I wasn't stuck and got to the patient.' Maryann too was not deterred when snow blocked her car:

> Two women came to the cottage at two in the morning to get me for a confinement and I couldn't move the car. So the three of us just had to walk.

Through the snow, we walked carrying the maternity case, each of us carrying it for a short period at a time, and trying to be as quick as possible. It was probably four miles away. It was the woman's fourth baby so we knew we had to hurry as she might not have had a long labour. We made it in time.

This nurse who was wakened in the middle of the night, and then had to walk in the snow to the patient and deliver her baby, was the same nurse who recalls in a later chapter being 'dead tired' at times, even though she was generally healthy. It was essential to be healthy in order to cope mentally and physically with all the challenges presented to them. Another problem that nurses contended with was their lack of time off duty.

On-call and Holidays

Nurses who worked in the 1940s, 50s and early 60s clearly had very little time off and even had to find their own holiday relief cover. Some nurses said they could work for as long as a year without an official day off. Nurses were aware of the needs of the community and their duty to be accessible for them. The amount of time off that the Hebridean nurses had may well have been different from their counterparts working on the mainland in the 1940s.

Effie remembers her lack of time off in the 1940s:

> At that time the district nurses were run by a committee. I had to report to the schoolmaster's wife who was in charge then. I had been working in Galashiels, and we had a day off every week but there were no set hours. Here you were on call all the time and I wasn't allowed a day off apart from my holidays. I had no outside life at all – in fact I had difficulty getting to church sometimes. I even tried to get to the prayer meeting that was on a Thursday morning at midday. It just lasted an hour and I did the visits that needed to be done in that area before I went. Some days I couldn't go of course, but when I could arrange my visits I went to the prayer meeting. But the first time I went the schoolmaster's wife objected to my having gone. I was supposed to be on duty and she objected to my going, and I told her that in any other area I worked in, I always had a half day off or time off provided I could organise my caseload.

Religion was important to the nurses of the islands and for many of them in Lewis their only social activity was attending church. It is interesting that this nurse who objected to having no time off was only in the area for three years and she then went to the mainland to work because of the 'difficulties' she was having.

Most nurses nevertheless accepted the limited time off as normal practice. Catherine worked for a year without a day off:

> I remember working here for a whole year without a day off, a whole year! It must have gone over a year. The superintendent in Inverness was quite appalled about the situation at the time. She couldn't find anyone to cover me and she said, "Just take some hours off when you can," and that's just the way

it went. You couldn't really be off call when there was no one else there but yourself. And you were quite happy doing it as long as you were able to do it.

Catherine did not complain about the lack of time off and accepted it as part of her job.

Morag in Scalpay also had a similar story to relate about her working hours:

> I couldn't tell you how many hours I worked because I tended to be on all the time. We only got a holiday once a year. Two weeks' holiday in my time. Nobody relieved us. Maybe there would be days when you were slack, when you didn't have so much to do and you relaxed a bit.

Some of the nurses had been relief nurses themselves. They too did not have much time off, even in the 1960s, but by then they at least had a day off a week as Neilina explains:

> It was a bone of contention, the full time district nurses had to have their day off and there was no thought to giving the relief a day off. It was the same with holidays, there wasn't any sensible consideration there for holidays, but all the time I was part time, and I wasn't full time.

Neilina had worked full time prior to her relief post, and describes her working time in the early 1960s:

> You came home and had a bite of lunch or something but you were maybe called out shortly. Then in the evening you sat there on call. You couldn't say that your day was over, sometimes you were not called out at all, but then sometimes you were. That was the position. There wasn't a set day off at all. You worked full time, we didn't even have a day off. On call twenty-four hours and we did triple duties.

The amount of time off the nurses had did increase. By the 1960s most nurses had an official day off once a week and a more systematic approach was introduced the following decade. Dolina, who worked in the town areas, describes the change in her time off:

> It was when 1974 reorganisation came. Previous to that you didn't know where everybody was on call, but after reorganisation we were able to work on a rota and it worked very well. How we did it was, we were allowed two days off a week, but prior to that you got off what you could take off and you could have worked a long time without days off. The new regime meant there was always one person on call, and we tried to work it out that you could at least be off the evening before your day off. There were so many returns (visits) then because there were no carers, so whoever was on call did the return visit and that was counted unsocial hours so it worked fine.

Nurses saw changes in their working conditions in the 1970s, giving them more time for themselves and no longer tying them to the district. The changes would have had implications for the community and how they perceived the 'new' working arrangement. Not all nurses were in favour of having so much time off. Neilina felt it could have a detrimental effect on the patients' care. She compared the care of the twentieth century to that of the twenty-first century and voiced her concern about various remote geographical areas not having midwifery cover. She felt that patients benefited from knowing they could call out a nurse during the night: 'If you were called out during the night it was usually to attend somebody who was very ill. It was a great comfort for the people to know that the district nurse was there and she could always be sent for'. We have seen district nursing slowly disappearing from remote areas, yet as Neilina maintains, it was a service valued by the public.

As would be expected on the islands, where religion was of importance, Sunday was usually a quieter day for nurses and they only carried out essential work. Ann recalls that although they had visits to carry out people would only call the nurse out if it was really necessary.

The working conditions of nurses from 1940 until 1974 were harsh, and would in many ways be considered unacceptable today. Although nurses complained about their own accommodation and, at times, their time off, they seemed to prioritise their patients' needs over their own. Regardless of the kind of house that their patients lived in, nurses carried out their duties. Every effort was made by nurses to reach their patients, whatever the weather; perhaps sometimes to the detriment of their own health and safety. It clearly required physical strength and courage on the part of nurses to cope with the dark walks in the night in all weathers. They were able to manage the long hours on duty and for some, long periods without days off or holidays. The district nurses' contribution to care in the Outer Hebrides was their total commitment to their patients, notwithstanding their difficult working environments and the many other obstacles they faced.

CHAPTER SIX

Relationships

Bernera bridge

Patients

In the days before mobile telephones and before landlines were installed in every nurse's house, patients were resourceful when they needed to contact the nurse. Generally, the community knew where the nurse was and nurses tell of leaving a notice in their window saying what time they would return, supposing they had to leave the village for any reason, such as to assist a colleague in the next area.

In 1953 a phone was installed in Rhoda's cottage, but it was a nuisance too. It was the only phone in the village and she was told time and again to 'leave the door open because we have to get to the phone if we need a doctor.' She recounts: 'It was a nuisance in a way and they would come in and ask if they could use the phone and you didn't like to refuse people.'

Often when people were looking for the nurse, whether during the day or night, they managed to find her. Little consideration was given to the nurse's own time or privacy. Maryann describes how patients contacted her 'by phone or sometimes they came to the bedroom window and knocked'. It was quite normal for patients to call at a house where the nurse was attending a patient to give her a message. Marion remembers:

> I was attending to an elderly lady when there was a knock on the door and a young
> lad asked to speak to me. He said, "You are needed in a house along the road." I said

I would finish what I was doing but he was insistent that I go and he said, "The baby has been born." On hearing this the *bodach* [old man] in the house said, "What on earth do you need the nurse for if the baby has already been born?"

The nurses were of a generation who would not offend anyone, even though it was inconvenient to be interrupted in their own home or the patient's home by members of the community.

When the nurse was 'off duty' it was still possible to locate her. Mairi recalls how a patient contacted her:

I remember going out with my father to cut peats and I had on one of my brother's boiler suits. A man came out to the moor to get me as a cow had stood on a woman's leg. I had to go in my boiler suit, despite it being my half day off. My mother's house was in the middle of the village and they could see if my car was there and if it wasn't there, she would know where I was.

Many patients' relatives walked a distance to contact the nurse and then travelled back with her to the patient as Maryann recalls: 'They had to walk in the snow from Tong and back again [approximately four miles each way]. It was usually the man that came for me, if there was a man in the house. He came and knocked at the door, or at the window, if I didn't hear the door'.

Until the early 1970s most communities in the Outer Hebrides could still contact the district nurse quite easily. Until the reorganisation of the health service in 1974, communities considered that the district nurse belonged to them. The nurses' accounts suggest that there was little regard to their time off or whether it was day or night; they were bound by the community's need of their service.

District nurse Bella Johnstone (Bellag Raghnaill), Eriskay, on the telephone. (Estate of Dr Kenneth Robertson)

The Community

Before the introduction of the health service in 1948 patients had to pay for the service of a nurse or doctor. Some nurses tried to avoid calling a doctor unless it was really urgent when they were in a home where there was obvious poverty. The community was relieved when it no longer had to pay for a doctor or a nurse. Marion recounts an amusing incident when she was on district during the time when each household was expected to pay for the service of the nurse:

> I was enjoying the lovely sunshine as I strolled up to Angus's house. He had diabetes and I visited him daily to give him his injection. He was an old bachelor and very easy going. As I got near the house I heard the noise of raised voices of men arguing. I wondered what I should do. If I did not go in I would have to go back later but I didn't want to go into a house where an argument was going on. I braced myself and although the door was open I knocked loudly. Angus came forward and said: "We were just talking about you, nurse." "What have I done?" I asked. "It's not that at all, but this man here tells me that for the two and sixpence that every household pays for the service of the nurse she's got to supply the bandages, all the disinfectant and the swabs she needs in that house and I am arguing with him that that is wrong. For two and six pence all you get is the nurse, naked as she is!"

Marion recalls that in her area there was one household which refused to pay 'airgead a nurse' (the money for the nurse). When the treasurer went to the house to get an explanation the man maintained that, "It's because it is years since a nurse was in this house." The response from the treasurer was, "Consider yourself a lucky man that your family didn't need a nurse."

District nurses in this book may have been lone workers, but they could call on the assistance of various people in the community; their neighbours, the minister, the police, their husband, or relatives of patients and ferrymen.

Chris recalls:

> When there was snow and you couldn't get the car out of the garage, usually somebody would come and there was always a good neighbour and the minister was also very helpful. Often in the mornings when I went out, the garage would be open, and there was the neighbour and the minister and they would be trying to start the car pushing it in and out of the road, which was very good of them. The car wouldn't start even without the snow sometimes.

It was clearly reassuring for the nurse who had car problems or was hampered by weather to have the willing assistance of the minister and the neighbour. Nurses appreciated the kindness of the community. Joan remembers: 'Everybody looked after you. There wasn't a house that I couldn't go into at any time. Calum, a neighbour, kept some peats for me which was needed to keep the fire going. The people were good to me. They made sure that I had my own peat stack at the side of the house.'

Dolina recalls a time when a member of the community stopped her in her tracks:

> I used to give an old lady an injection every day. This particular day, a cold horrible raw day, I was walking on my way back and a lady was standing at the gate of her house. She beckoned me to her and said, "Come in here I'm wanting to speak to you …"
>
> "Well I can't stay just now; I have patients waiting for me," I said.
>
> "Let them wait, there is not a lot you can do." So in I went in and the table was set. "Sit there and take a cup of tea, take your time, you're going there like a hare. Sit! Anyway, what kind of shoes have you got on there, why have you not got right shoes on?" All about my welfare! "Why have you not got a scarf on your neck?" She came with a scarf stinking of mothballs and wrapped it round my neck. I had to wear it all day until I got home. It was warm but smelly!

On one occasion a vigilant and caring community prevented a tragedy as Rebecca remembers:

> I was coming home at the end of my day's work when the car just skidded off the road into a loch. I must say it wasn't a deep loch, but the car could have sunk down. I really got a fright! One of the men working on the road had seen the car opposite his house on the road and when it didn't appear again on the next hill he knew something must have happened. So he came with a squad of men, but by the time they came I had managed to free myself. I sat there wondering what was going to happen to me, but these boys managed to get me and the car out.

Although nurses were at the community's beck and call, the community in turn looked after their wellbeing. The relationship between the nurse and her patients was clearly a reciprocal one. Mairi recalls there always being a woman, usually a neighbour, who would come to see if she needed help when a baby was being born. On the other hand, Rebecca remembers that relatives who were doing most of the caring at home could sometimes be sharp with the nurse:

> I always felt that the relatives do the caring most of the time and they can be on edge sometimes. Maybe if you were a few minutes late they would be there waiting and not too happy. You had to remember that they had the brunt of the caring and that if they were irritable, they had reason to be. You had to take that sometimes. Take it in your stride and not react.

Nurses who worked on an island without a bridge depended on the ferrymen day and night to take them to and from the island. It was also the responsibility of the nurse to arrange transport for the doctor, if he was required, and to accompany a patient to hospital. The nurse had to organise her own transport back to the island if she visited patients in surrounding areas or if she had to go to the hospital with a patient. On the island of Bernera, Joan had a unique way of contacting Suley, who was the ferryman:

He would be there most of the time and he told me that if he wasn't there I was to pick up a stone and throw it on the tank beside the pier night or day – even three in the morning and he would hear it. He then got up from bed and took the ferry out. I used the stone often. I had to get back to the cottage on the island after time off, or taking a patient to hospital, and that was when I needed the stone. It was a big tank and the pier was beside it.

On the island of Scalpay nurses were looked after by the ferrymen, as Nora recounts: 'When I had to go to the hospital in Stornoway to collect stores or accompany a patient there, I had to phone from the hospital to tell the ferry boys that I was leaving and they would then time it for the ferry to meet me and they did not charge me'.

Nora also praised the service of the ferrymen when speaking of the assistance she received from the community:

There was an accident in the village and a tourist injured her leg, so I got two of the young men in the area and one of them had a wee van, and I asked them to come with me to the clinic to get a stretcher and a few crepe bandages and splints. The boys went with me and carried the stretcher with the woman into her car. I had decided that it would be quicker if her husband drove her in his car to the hospital as it would take some time for an ambulance to fetch her and then take her the forty-mile journey to hospital. I then went to the nearest house and while I was phoning the doctor, I also phoned the ferry boys, who were home for lunch and asked them if they would take the ferry before its scheduled time and of course they agreed.

It is obvious that on an island with neither doctor nor bridge, the community assisted the nurse to provide care. However, Rebecca who worked on the same island, describes why she was reluctant to contact the ferrymen, especially at night, to transport a doctor to see a patient:

The main thing was that we were dependent on a ferry, sometimes in the winter the last ferry would be at six o'clock at night. If I had to get the doctor, it wasn't just the doctor you were getting it was the ferry as well. It put the onus on you. I felt it was far too much really because you had to consider the relatives. You were called maybe to an old woman and in your opinion, she didn't really need to see a doctor but the relatives were all worried and it was their right that a doctor should see their mother. So you had to weigh all this up, and then weigh the ferrymen's reaction to be got out of their bed, and you hated to do it.

Rebecca was the only nurse who mentioned that she was apprehensive about calling the ferrymen. It was she too who commented that she was glad to leave the island with no doctor, as she disliked the extra responsibility. Interestingly, she was also the only nurse working on an island with no doctor who was not trained as a Queen's Nurse. Her worry about being called out in this situation may have been due to her lack of training or lack of confidence in herself, which the Queen's Nurses certainly had.

The reciprocity described in these accounts between the nurse and the community would be unthinkable in the twenty-first century, where island communities are so varied and people are less dependent on each other. It could be argued however that the community's expectation of the nurse at the time was both demanding and excessive.

The relationship with the community was identified as a source of support, yet tensions were acknowledged, as some of the nurses noted. They found that it was necessary to maintain a professional relationship with the community as Chris explains: 'I didn't make any friends in the area; well not close friends that I could go to at any time. It wouldn't be wise to.' Despite Joan stating that she could go to any house in the village, it was clear that most nurses did not have close personal relationships with people in the area they worked.

A study published in 2003 found that district nurses continued to have problems with being part of the community. It was suggested that one of the reasons for this involved notions surrounding respect for the nurse as a professional. Even thirty years on from the time these nurses were working, some 'community nurses' continued to have problems with being part of the community and maintaining their professionalism.

Husbands

As previously stated, nurses who married in the 1940s and the 1950s usually had to leave work. There were exceptions to the 'rule'; for instance Margaret, who was 'allowed to carry on working as her husband was working at sea'. Mary perceived that boyfriends were accepted before husbands:

> The husbands weren't approved at that time but the boyfriends were. I was older, I was thirty-six by the time I got married and there were no children about. It was quite annoying [for my husband] if he thought that we were going to go somewhere and then he had to trail out in the snow with me to a confinement. If you did deliver a baby, and your husband had been waiting many hours for you in the car, sometimes he was called into the house and got a whisky from the father of the baby.

Nurses described how their husbands were an important help to them after nurses were 'allowed' to marry. Many husbands acted as chauffeurs, especially in the winter when the roads could be dangerous. As one nurse remarks: 'A husband wasn't supposed to live in the nurse's cottage but they came in handy for starting the car in the mornings'.

Isobel's husband taught his wife to drive, rowed her across the loch to attend a maternity patient when the roads were blocked with snow, accompanied her on her rounds in bad weather and on all night calls, as well as having her meals ready for her after work. Isobel worked in the 1960s and it was then becoming more acceptable to have husbands staying with the nurse, either in the cottage or in their own home.

General Practitioners (GPs)

Nurses and doctors have always worked closely together to complement each other's care of patients, but they have at times had difficulty understanding each other's role, or being able to work effectively with each other. Florence Nightingale wrote that the chief qualities doctors expected from nurses were 'devotion and obedience'. Even when the NHS was set up in 1948 the British Medical Association (BMA) wanted 'more nurses of adequate skill and a capacity to follow doctor's orders'. Many doctors wanted the devoted assistant and handmaiden who had been available before the war years. From the twentieth century and before, doctors dictated the nurse's role and had input into the delivery of her training. Jessie remembers receiving most of her theoretical training from doctors during her nursing training in the 1940s. It is therefore not surprising that within the nurse-doctor relationship almost all the power was weighted in favour of doctors, leaving nurses in a subservient role.

In 1967 Leonard Stein wrote an article entitled 'The Doctor-Nurse Game', in which he postulated that the interaction between the two professions involved the nurse making recommendations to the doctor about clinical issues, yet appearing passive. The 'game' supported and protected a structure where the physician was in clear authority. The power relationship between the nurse and the doctor is complex. Sociological explanations, feminist theories and economic explanations have been explored to uncover the attitudes presented by both doctor and nurse. Stein also agreed that the relationship between doctor and nurse was more complex than might be first imagined and suggested that if doctors were going to make decisions based on the best information possible they could not afford to ignore nursing knowledge.

The model of the doctor and the district nurse working closely together in the mid-1920s was recognised as one to be replicated by Mary Breckinridge in Kentucky. It is surprising to find that, only twenty years later, not all nurses had a close working relationship with the doctor, as some nurses recall. Nevertheless, they did not hesitate to contact the doctor if they thought it was necessary.

Christina was a confident woman who did not hesitate to phone for a doctor when she was attending a confinement, as she recalls:

> I sent for the doctor because when I was examining for the foetal heartbeat, I felt that it wasn't quite right. The GP came and he wasn't in a good mood either and the first thing I told him was that I had called him because I had two patients in labour and that I wasn't happy with this patient's foetal heart. He examined the mother and he said that there was nothing wrong as far as he could see. I said, "You will have to stay here because I'm going to see what the other labouring woman is doing." I came back and shortly after that the child was delivered and it was blue. He was there … I made him stay. I don't think he liked having to stay with the patient while I went away and while I delivered the baby. I didn't care, but I don't think he liked it … oh I didn't care, no way. If he had left me then there would have been trouble … I told him straight to the point, he had to come; he jolly well had to come, because I certainly didn't send for a doctor without a reason.

This shows that Christina cared more about her patient's wellbeing than about upsetting the doctor. There was no subservience in this situation; both the doctor and the nurse had their work to do, and the nurse had responsibility to the patient. Christina was in control of the situation.

Dolina, who had delivered a baby that died, stated that 'she had been glad when the GP had come immediately when she sent for him'. She recalls a conversation she had with a relief nurse shortly after the incident:

> A relief nurse came to cover me for my holidays. She was just straight out of district training and I'd left her a note of four patients due their babies before I came back. I gave her the doctor's phone number and I said, "Don't hesitate to call them at any time; they will be more than willing to help." "Och!" she said, "I can't be fussed with doctors." I said, "Nurse, you won't be very long in this job when you realise that they are the very best friends you've got." She had the confidence of youth but experience teaches you.

If a nurse needed to contact a GP and no phone was nearby she had to be imaginative with the message she gave someone to relay to the GP, so that he would understand the urgency of the situation. Christine managed both. She was attending a woman during the night who was having her first baby and there was no phone in the house. The foetal heart started to be irregular and she was not quite ready to deliver: 'I had to send the husband to the telephone box with a note to call the GP and say, "FH" (foetal heart). I didn't want to worry the husband. The doctor came and she had to have a forceps delivery. The baby was ok.'

Nurses cared for the family as a whole and tried to avoid causing alarm. The testimonies show the district nurses to be confident women who took their responsibilities seriously and put the needs of their patients first, which sometimes resulted in conflict with the GP. Communication with the GP was essential in remote areas and the majority of nurses spoke of a trusting relationship with the doctor and their dependency on them, especially when they were working alone on a small island.

From the 1950s onwards many nurses had phones in their cottage or nearby where they could contact the doctor. However, on the smaller islands it was also necessary for the nurse to arrange a ferry for the doctor to come across to see the patients. Some nurses said that they worked closely with the GP while others only saw him when they called him to a patient. Rebecca comments on her relationship with the GP:

> On the phone mostly, and of course at that time if the GP came down to see a patient day or night, we had to meet him, he didn't take his car across. We had to go to the patient with him. When I first went onto the district I didn't realise that the onus was on me to try and persuade the doctor to come down. I used to think I'll tell him the symptoms, I'll tell him what I think and then it's up to him to make the decision. The doctor we had then was nearing retirement, and he wouldn't always come unless you actually asked him. Oh I learned – I had to!

Rebecca had difficulty calling the GP when she went to the island at first and but she learned that she was the one that had to make the decision about whether the doctor was necessary. Explaining the patient's symptoms not enough – she had to actually ask the GP to come out to see the patient.

It was expected that there would be less contact with the GP on the smaller islands than on the larger ones. Marion, who worked in Lewis, complained that it was not always easy to contact the doctor and that communication with him was not always good. She recalls having problems contacting the doctor on a Sunday: 'He was a churchman and I couldn't take him out of the pulpit on Sunday as he was preaching. He would never say where he was but his housekeeper knew where he was and I was glad I never had an emergency on a Sunday'.

Other nurses complained that doctors: 'would come if there was a complication'; 'were often not available. It could be trying that way'; 'wasn't keen on going out at night unless it was really desperate'; 'always came out if I phoned him and I was worried about a patient'; 'did not communicate much with the nurses at all'.

Marion tells of a GP who had an unusual routine after a baby was born: 'He liked alcohol and after a confinement he always toasted the baby's health, wealth and happiness. On one occasion he pushed me so that the table with the bottle of whisky was hidden from the mother; he then helped himself to more.'

Christina, the nurse above who refused to allow the doctor to leave the patient, did not appear to be subservient to the doctor. However, it is likely that some of these nurses, who were trained within the medical model of nursing in the 1940s and 1950s, still retained the attitude of the 'doctor's handmaiden', which the Briggs Report identified as being the public perception of nursing in 1972. Although nurses describe the bad practices of doctors, they do not appear to have challenged their behaviour.

Kate recounts a funny story of a time in Uist when she had a student doctor accompany her on her rounds. They visited an elderly man who had asthma and was taking a drug called Franol:

> For some strange reason we all referred to the tablets as F tablets even when ordering them. When we were leaving the patient, and halfway down the stairs he shouted after us, "Nurse, what about my F tablets?" The young doctor thought he was swearing and said, "He's a very cantankerous old fellow isn't he?" I had the tablets in the car and had forgotten to take them into the house!

Most nurses had a good working relationship with the GPs but some only saw the doctor when he was contacted to deal with complex medical needs. This relationship may have been difficult for the nurse if she did not have a working relationship with him, and then had to depend on his medical expertise within a clinical situation. It is likely that in this period medicine would have prominence in the health hierarchy. Despite the nurses' disapproval of the actions of GPs who behaved unprofessionally, the situation was accepted.

Colleagues

Most nurses in this period did not have nursing colleagues but depended mainly on the GP and the community. By the mid-1970s a wider range of health and social care workers became available. Only Dolina had experience of working in a team of nurses as she worked in the town area of Stornoway in the late 1970s, after health care reorganisation.

Most nurses recall having very little contact with colleagues, apart from when they relieved one another, or when they needed help, during a busy period as Ann explains:

> My colleague in the next area relieved me when I had time off … they would send for her when I was off and they would send for me when she was off. There would be a note on the door of the cottage to inform people who came looking for the nurse who was on duty and how they could contact her.

Marion recalls: 'There were no phones. If I was needed in the nurse's area, due to maybe having two maternity patients going at the same time or her being off ill, I got a telegram.'

Nurses described how they depended on colleagues when busy with more than one midwifery confinement at the same time. It would take forward planning to have time to send a telegram to the nurse's colleague that more than one birth was imminent. Christina recalls only knowing the nurse in the next area as a friend and not a colleague: 'The nurse in the next area and I trained in Queen's together, so I got to know her.'

In the 1970s when staff meetings were convened, the heavy workload did not allow the nurses to attend, as Dolina recalls: 'Work was so heavy, it was so busy, you didn't have time. There were not enough beds in the hospital and all the nursing work was done at home and we had ill people. But we used to have staff meetings occasionally when time allowed.' On the other hand, the contact with the nurse supervisors was mandatory.

Superintendent of Nurses

The inspection of Queen's Nurses was carried out by a superintendent, or 'Inspectress', as she is referred to in the minutes of the LNSSC. Superintendents periodically inspected each Queen's Nurse by accompanying the nurse to see patients and observing how various procedures were carried out. They also listened to the nurses' concerns, and before the introduction of the NHS, conveyed any problems to the Local Nursing Association. During the Queen's Nurse training the nurse was regularly accompanied and assessed by the superintendent. Comments were documented about the nurses' appearance in uniform, their relationship with patients and their clinical skills. Examples of comments in the inspection reports for a Miss Maclean, a Miss Macleod and a Miss Macdonald included:

> Miss M is absolutely dependable, gentle, kind and one of the most faithful women I have ever had. (1947)

Miss M looks neat and smart in uniform and her books and cards are well kept. (1953)

Miss M being tall and slim, is extremely smart in uniform, she has a frank and pleasant manner. (1966)

Miss M is a tall, rather stoutly built nurse and a dependable person with a homely, pleasant manner. (1950)

It is interesting that the comments did not always relate to the nurse's care and professionalism towards the patients. Not all comments were complimentary as the following shows:

Miss M is a tall, healthy looking nurse whose work has been very average. To teach her to be methodical in district work has been very difficult and even now is still not up to standard. (1953)

Miss M moves and acts with a slow measured pace and her manner is rather stiff and aloof. The teaching aspect has so far failed to interest her. In appearance she is tall with a good carriage and a tidy clean look. Her staid, slow manner is rather striking. (1956)

Miss M's work and manner in the home is dull and lacking in stimulus and interest. The quality of her work is fair and the technical procedure is used in a stereotypical fashion. She is slow to realise the wide scope of her responsibilities and requires guidance and encouragement in that direction. She is tall well-proportioned in build and tidy in her dress. (1957)

It is unlikely that in the twenty-first century assessments of such personal nature would be considered acceptable.

Morag remembers two amusing incidents when she was carrying out her Queen's district nurse training in Edinburgh:

The war was still on and food was terribly, terribly scarce. One of the nurses went out on her visits with the superintendent for her assessment. She attended to her first patient who suffered from diabetes and had an insulin injection before her breakfast. When they were leaving the patient said, "Oh nurse, your breakfast is in the oven." When we all went back to the office in Castle Terrace for lunch that day the three nurses who worked in the area that the superintendent had visited were all called to the office and reprimanded for taking food in a patient's house. The superintendent knew which nurses were allocated to each patient therefore all the nurses who had visited this particular patient were reprimanded for eating in a patient's home, a practice not viewed as acceptable.

Morag trained in the 1940s and recalls that because food was scarce, having breakfast in the home of a patient with diabetes was accepted as normal; so much so that the other nurses were 'envious of the nurses who had diabetic patients'.

In the second incident Morag herself was called to the office by the superintendent, to receive praise for caring for a patient. However:

> The superintendent said, "There has been a message from the nursing home to thank you for your prompt attention [she had diagnosed a lady with an ectopic pregnancy] and they have sent you a gift of five pounds, but you can't have it, you are not allowed to take money. You can accept a pair of stockings or a box of handkerchiefs." Five pounds were like fifty today. So that was no food, no money!

Superintendents were also assigned to the nurse's geographical areas and carried out supervision regularly. It would seem that every area was supervised differently as Jessie indicates:

> A woman came here, a Miss Weir [the same who crops up regularly in the LNSSC minutes during the 1940s]. I never forgot her, from England, a supervisor. She accompanied you on your visits. Now I wasn't Queen's trained but she came round with everyone on district periodically, about every year, and then she told you what you should or shouldn't do. That was a help and she looked at your books. She was very helpful. There was also a committee in the area and they were very involved, like the board of management. Just a few men and women and they were the ones that decided if you got, say, a bicycle.

Jessie's appointment as a district nurse is documented in the LNSSC minutes of 1946 where she is described as 'aged twenty-six, SRN, SCM and unemployed'. She was pleased to have the superintendent giving her advice about her practice but she commented more negatively on the local nursing committee who made decisions about nurses' working conditions.

Nurses who worked around the 1950s continued to receive visits from the superintendent as Maryann remembers: 'I had a superintendent coming from Edinburgh yearly at that time and we had to go round to see one or two patients with her just to see that everything was done according to the rules.'

A Miss Clyne is mentioned in the minutes of the Queen's Nursing Institute in 1956 as being responsible for 'five nurses in five areas'. The Nursing Mirror (1948) included an article in which the editor accompanied Miss Clyne, the superintendent, on her rounds to Uist to see the district nurses. The article describes Miss Clyne as 'the County superintendent who looked after the professional and personal interests of the district nurses.' It mentions that nurses were 'one of the strong links in this successful HIMS.'

Lena was very pleased to have her practice supervised:

> She [the superintendent] checked you did everything as it should be done. She watched you doing everything like carrying out the wound dressings and the injections. I did one wound dressing that was going to be difficult, and I was glad of that later on because she gave me advice.

The Queen's Nurse Training was discontinued in 1968. It was evident that inspection was routine in the 1940s, 50s and early 60s and nurses appeared to value the advice and support of the superintendents. With only the visits from the superintendent to ensure nursing standards were maintained, most nurses were working autonomously.

Health Visitors

Only three of the nurses interviewed here worked with health visitors. Although they were well established in the mainland of Scotland it was not until after the reorganisation of the health service in 1974 that they were employed in the Outer Hebrides. A review of health visiting in the islands was carried out in 1984, and stated: 'It is now eight years since this service was introduced.' In this period there were no health visitors, nevertheless, some nurses did comment on their introduction in around 1976.

Catherine recalls working in the 1960s: 'There were no health visitors then, and we had the health visiting to do as well as our general and midwifery caseload'. She was not too happy when health visitors were introduced into her area:

> I was a bit peeved that they were only writing things down. They weren't hands-on as we were used to doing. You just got into it and that was that, and I probably resented them a wee bit. And I also thought what a waste of time just putting comments on paper. Just do something about the problems and that's it.

On the other hand, Nora was delighted when the health visitor arrived: 'I was glad when we got a health visitor because her caseload was the whole of Harris and Scalpay. I was really glad because she took a load off me, and she was a very pleasant person and we got on well. But people were a bit wary, especially the patients.' Marion recalls: 'We were desperate to get health visitors because they were in cities like Glasgow and were such a help to relieve the nurse's caseload.'

Health visitors were not part of the nurse's lives until the 1970s, and most district nurses carried out triple duty which included child development, immunization and school inspection. It is therefore no surprise that some nurses were looking forward to their introduction to the Outer Hebrides.

CHAPTER SEVEN

Patients and Poultices

Priorities and Caseloads

Most nurses reported that it was the patient confined to bed or dependent on others who had priority on visits, second only to a midwifery patient, who was always their first priority. Christine describes the changes that took place in the number of patients she saw and the reason she visited them:

> At the beginning when I started in 1957 I didn't have so many [patients]. They were all GNCs [general nursing care], bathing, injections and dressings. … near the end of my nursing I had more of a caseload. We called in to see people and advised them and saw elderly people. We didn't have midwifery; they all seemed to go to hospital whereas in the early days midwifery was the bulk of our work. I went to see terminally ill patients first. Of course if we had a mother who had come out of hospital, I would go and see her first. We were on duty I suppose twenty-four hours. Our day started around nine usually. In the later years [late 1970s] we used to meet the doctor in the surgery every week and discuss the week's work. We finished work at different times but if there weren't any problems it was about five. Sometimes earlier, sometimes busy and sometimes not so busy. I remember going out for more than a year every night at 9 o'clock to somebody who was bedridden and he didn't have much help. Maybe in between times of course I had terminally ill people or people who had suffered strokes; I had to visit them quite often. If people were bed ridden, we would have to go to visit them first and wash them and dress them and get them up, and there was plenty of that before the carers came along.

Details of the general nursing care to which the nurses refer were given in the Queen's Nursing booklet:

> … the professional care given by a nurse to a patient according to his/her necessity, to meet some of his/her basic needs includes; washing and attention to details of toilet, bed making, with special consideration for his/her comfort and the prevention of bedsores or deformity, arrangement of the room and his/her accessories for his/her convenience, advice on nutrition and hygiene generally and relief of pain.

Health care has changed considerably since the 1940s and 1950s; a fact echoed by Chrissie when she was asked about how she prioritised her caseload at that time:

> I would go to an old lady who was on her own or somebody who was ill and near the end of their days and that could go on for quite a while. Also people were more inclined to stay in bed in those days, especially older people. I remember going to one lady very frequently, she was bedridden, but I don't think she would be bedridden the way things are today. People were encouraged to go to bed with minor ailments which they wouldn't do today.

Although there are similarities in the geographical areas the nurses covered, each one had a unique story to relate regarding her caseload. Catriona recalls:

> When I started on my district there was a man very ill with chest cancer and I had to go to him daily and manage a chest drain which could be difficult. He was my first patient and after that the rest were just ordinary patients requiring general nursing care. If people were bedridden they had to be washed, toenails cut – no podiatrist then on the island. You really did what was necessary, changing beds, that sort of thing. With terminally ill patients I often stayed with them all night especially if they were elderly and there was nobody else with them. I dressed the body when they died.

Catriona also recalls being asked by the doctor to stay all night with a lady who was pregnant and had been bleeding. She accepted the request as normal, which may indicate that it was a regular occurrence.

Rebecca, who provided holiday relief to a nurse on a small island during the 1960s, describes her caseload when she was first on call, comparing it to her experience of a larger island where there was a doctor available:

> I would say about ten patients a day and most of it was maybe somebody bedridden, general nursing care, diabetics and leg ulcers, we had a lot of that. The caseload wasn't heavy in itself; it was more the other side of it, such as being called out. We had lots of night calls and then, as I say, diagnosing and wondering if we needed to send for the doctor and that was the major part of the work. I would go out in the morning, never went out earlier than ten, because people weren't ready for you, and then I would come home for lunch and maybe I would have a call or two in the afternoon and sometimes not, but you had to stay by the phone in case you were wanted, the workload was not heavy really. I was there for twenty years. Tarbert was a heavy, heavy district and the places are so far apart. I would do mileage of sometimes 100 miles a day. The doctors got first call there all the time, whereas in Scalpay it was the nurse. Nobody ever phoned the doctor direct. I would never have gone back to Scalpay in pre-bridge days.

Part of the nurse's duties on an island with no doctor was the distribution of medicines to patients, as Jean describes:

> I was sent over to give relief. It was the ferry in those days. And the doctor used to go over once a week to do a surgery on the island and he would go

back to Tarbert, sort out all the tablets in a box, put them on the ferry the next day to Scalpay and the nurse had to deliver all the medicines to the patients. And it so happened that I arrived the day after the doctor had been, so he had gone back to Tarbert and the box came. I went to the ferry and collected the box of medicines. When I got back to the house I opened the box. Lo and behold a bottle of Aludrox [liquid medicine, white in colour] had broken in the box. Can you imagine all these tablets with labels covered with Aludrox and my first day there! I thought this is not right! I phoned the surgery in Tarbert and spoke to the receptionist, who was the doctor's wife and told her what had happened. I told her that on some of the bottles I can't make out the labels, some have no labels and I don't know the patients. Between the two of us, I don't know how long we spent, we sorted it all out, and then I had to go round all these patients and pray I was giving out the right tablets.

Nurses were taught about the administration of medicines during their training and were aware 'never to give medicines from unlabelled bottles or other containers' and that misappropriation of drugs was viewed very seriously. However, the reality of working life did not always match up with what the nurse has been taught during her training.

Nurses had to be adaptable. Morag recalls the effect on her caseload when an outbreak of whooping cough affected the children of one of the smaller islands in 1951:

There were four or five elderly people in their eighties who needed general nursing care and who died in my time and we had to do the last offices and everything like that and I was on the go all the time. There were the GNCs and there were confinements and you had to follow up after the birth because there was no health visitor. When I was on the island before the injections for whooping cough came, the school was closed, all the children were down with whooping cough and I had to be out night and day. I'll always remember that year. I had to get up once or twice a night. There was epistaxis [nose bleeds] and the cough was bad. Thank God, nobody died, that's what I always thank God for, that nobody died while I was there, in my care anyway.

Nurses taught the patients how to carry out treatments and care when they were not there. Mary recalls how lack of instruction caused some distress for a family she visited:

It was in the late 1970s and the doctor asked me how a patient who had constipation was getting on with the medicine prescribed. The doctor had prescribed suppositories [which] … looked like a plastic bullet! I asked the *cailleach* [old lady] how her husband was and she responded, "He is in pain and the doctor told him to repeat the suppositories again. He could not swallow them, but he first tried with cold water and then when he tried to swallow them with hot water they melted." They just didn't realise what they had to do with them. It was funny in a way but showed how much you had to teach the patients.

Nurse Cathie M. Maclennan.
(Bernera Historical Society)

Triple duty nursing describes the role of most of these nurses. It was carried out mainly in rural areas where one person undertook the work of the district nurse, midwife and health visitor. The scope of practice of the district nurse who was carrying out triple duty nursing was wide-ranging and involved all ages of the population. Nurses spoke of attending women before they had their baby, for ten days afterwards and then regularly for child development assessments. After the reorganization of the health service in 1974 and the introduction of health visitors only a few triple duty nurses were employed in rural areas, although there were still some employed in rural areas in the Outer Hebrides in the 1980s. The district nurse's practice would have been comparable, whether working in the city or a remote area, but these nurses faced challenges associated with the significant remoteness of their geographical areas.

Unconventional Practice

Nurses felt they were well trained but often faced unusual situations which their training had not prepared them for. Improvisation was sometimes needed and necessity became the mother of invention, even at a birth. On one occasion Morag had to rush to attend a delivery but realised she had left sterile instruments at another mother's house:

I had delivered the baby and when I looked to get my scissors to cut the cord, I realised I had left the scissors in the last house. I asked if they had scissors and some lady came with a pair of scissors. They were rusty! So I got the kidney dish and I set fire to it first with spirit and then I poured Dettol on it and I thought here goes, but everything was fine and nothing happened. There was no sign of postnatal infection.

As mentioned before, nurses distributed cod liver oil and orange juice to mothers. These were provided by the Ministry of Food, which instructed district nurses to 'impress upon mothers the benefits which would accrue to them and their offspring by taking more of the oil and juices offered particularly during their period of pregnancy.'

Marion found an innovative way of administering the cod liver oil, which the Ministry of Food could not have envisaged:

The baby was so under nourished I used to soak cotton wool in cod liver oil and apply it to the skin. I believed that it was the vitamins in the cod liver oil that were being absorbed by the skin. Now the doctor didn't know what I had done and when he did his monthly visit he came along to the cottage where we had a baby clinic and said in surprise, "That baby is still alive." I said, "Oh yes, the baby is improving." He said, "I noticed, but she has got an awful fishy smell." He didn't know what I had been doing. Obviously it helped because the baby could take very little by mouth. It had what we would call 'marasmus' at one time, undernourished dry skin. That was the word that was used and we used to get quite a lot of babies like that. I don't remember ever using it in hospital, but it was just a case of, I can't give anything him by mouth so will try if he absorbs it through the skin.

Marasmus is translated as intra-uterine growth retardation. The nurse was improvising in carrying out this 'treatment' on the baby, which was not thriving. She chose not to inform the doctor about what she did, indicating that this was probably not an accepted treatment at the time.

It has been suggested by some writers that the relative isolation of the district nurses in some areas increased the possibility that they might develop idiosyncratic practices that were not based on contemporary procedures. In addition, procedures at the time would frequently have been based on custom and practice rather that research evidence. Most of the district nurses relied on nursing journals to update their skills. It is unlikely that the technique that Marion used was evidence based. Yet she believed that she had saved the baby's life. Marion was certainly innovative as on another occasion she also used a poultice of cattle feed as a treatment for a patient:

They had no oatmeal in the house, so I used cattle feed which they had. I stayed up all night making the poultices. I mixed it with hot water, but it was a never ending job, it would only stay warm for minutes and you had to have another one to put on. I would stand over the fire to heat it and then, twenty minutes later, you would need to change it. We used poultices for any infections of the skin. But then penicillin came and that was an amazing treatment for all infections.

Marion contributed to a book about traditional plant lore, in which she referred to the incident with the cattle feed poultice. The patient was the most seriously ill that she had encountered, a ten-year-old boy with pneumonia. She explained in the book how the poultice was placed between sheets and placed on the boy's back and chest, changing them every twenty minutes. She also made the child drink as much as he could to allow him to sweat. She said in the book that she 'stayed up all night making poultices and the child survived.'

Ceatag, in her working notes from the Outer Hebrides in 1947, speaks of how she made up a poultice with melted margarine on a piece of lint. It was used to relieve sores or boils on the feet 'as most people went around bare footed as shoes were few and far between'. The poultice was applied to the area whilst it was still hot, and when it cooled another one was applied, until the boil or sore burst and the pus drained. 'Sunlight soap with sugar then removed all the infection. Later we gave penicillin for such ailments but I also believed in applying sugar and hot boracic lint to a boil.'

Nursing textbooks from the 1950s and 1960s include poultices as a treatment, mainly for infections of the skin. They could be prepared using linseed, kaolin, charcoal, starch or even sometimes ice. There was no reference to oatmeal or margarine poultices in the textbooks, or evidence that oatmeal was therapeutic when taken orally.

Catriona however, also describes the use of oatmeal as a treatment:

> There was one patient that I was quite worried about after she had her baby. I called the doctor as she was bleeding heavily. The doctor was very good and we got the bleeding stopped and he told me to stay with the patient for the rest of the night, which I did. The doctor ordered the woman to have warm [oatmeal] gruel and she had to drink it.

Accepting that the doctor knew what he was doing, Catriona did not question him, which might indicate that this 'treatment' may have been used before. This book indicates that nurses did sometimes improvise their own 'cures' and that their own experiential knowledge was of value alongside medical prescription and traditional practice.

Although there is no evidence found in nursing textbooks regarding the therapeutic oral administration of oatmeal as a medicinal treatment, the tradition of its use in the Outer Hebrides may be over two hundred years old. As far back as the 1700s, when Martin Martin wrote about his visit to the island of Lewis, oatmeal was recognised as having therapeutic properties. Martin mentions '*Brochan*' as being oatmeal and boiled water, which he maintained the people used as a diuretic, a sedative and as a common cure for coughs. This remedy may have continued to be used in the Outer Hebrides. A writer of traditional medicines in the Highlands and Islands also found that oatmeal was often resorted to as a medicinal therapy and the gruel was used as a sedative and a diuretic.

Schools

In addition to the general nursing and unconventional care that the nurses provided to the community, their remit extended to caring for school children. The 1907 Education (Administration Provisions) Act required authorities to provide for the medical inspection of children, making the Board of Education a health authority. In this way the School Health Service emerged. Subsequently the number of health visitors required to assist in the school service rose from 600 to more than 2000 between 1914 and 1918 in England and Wales. Medical inspection of children continued until 1959 when the Ministry of Health no longer required a specific number of health checks on school children. However, school checks continued in most geographical areas and in the Outer Hebrides remained as part of the remit of district nurses until health visitors were introduced in the 1970s. In Barvas school records reveal that district nurses visited schools for a variety of reasons. For example, in June 1940 it is recorded that 'the district nurses examined the children and a consignment of gas masks that had been delivered was to be looked after by the nurse'. Her monthly visits are documented, as well as her visits to the school with the GP who examined and inspected the children. It is recorded that a child was excluded from school on account of a skin infection.

The school records of 1942 and 1943 in Barvas also reveal that Miss Weir, the superintendent of the district nurses, carried out half yearly visits. Examples of why she visited the school are recorded as: 'to address the pupils on how to prevent colds', and talking to classes on 'the laws of health and kindred subjects'. It is likely that it was the same Miss Weir who featured in the Lewis sub- committee minutes until 1947, advocating for improved nurses' working conditions and who also acted as supervisor for some of the nurses.

Most nurses found their school visits enjoyable. Catherine recalls: 'The schools were very interesting. I went to each school once a month checking heads, nails and bits and pieces. The medical officer came a few times a year and the children got their immunisations when she came.' Anna, who worked in the 1950s, recalls the number of schools she had to visit: 'I had ten schools to look after and check once a month. There was a school in every village. There were a lot of children then in all the schools.'

Schools were put under increased pressure as a result of the baby boom in the 1950s. In the Outer Hebrides there was a school in each village, and the increase of pupils would have impacted on the nurse's caseload. If she had to visit schools at least once a month, and accompany the doctor and possibly the superintendent every six months, this would involve a considerable amount of work when she already had a caseload of general nursing and midwifery care.

CHAPTER EIGHT

Travelling People

Travellers' Tales

One aspect of practice, which many of the nurses recalled with some affection, was caring for travellers at various camps in and around Stornoway, as well as on the mainland of Scotland. While it is said that the Scottish travellers are the descendants of vagrants and victims of the great famine or the Highland Clearances, it is forgotten, according to the anthropologist Judith Oakley, that the early 'Egyptians' (gypsies) were recorded in Scotland. She maintains that the term 'traveller' does not imply a 'drop out' from the sedentary society but full membership of an ethnic group. Often Scottish and Irish travellers tend to adopt the terminology 'gypsy'. They are sometimes labelled 'tinkers' and although they use this term among themselves they more often use the less pejorative term 'traveller'. For example, the only time the word 'tinker' is used in Betsy Whyte's book, *The Yellow on the Broom*, an account of her life travelling throughout Scotland in the early decades of the twentieth century, it is in a derogatory way. In the Outer Hebrides, travellers were known in Gaelic as the '*ceàrdan*' (craftsmen) and lived in different locations around the main town of Stornoway. Anecdotal evidence suggests that some lived in tents, some in caravans, while others were in small houses or huts, usually on the outskirts of the villages.

Many of the Scottish travellers' songs and stories were recorded by Hamish Henderson and others in the 1950s and have now been preserved and are available to listen to on the '*Tobar an Dulchais*'/'Kist o' Riches' website.

Morag, who carried out her training with the Queen's Institute in the 1940s, recalls the following incident in central Scotland:

> The superintendent, she had been a Queen's Nurse said, "The tinkers were here booking a nurse today and you will be their nurse. I believe that the tinkers always have a retained placenta!" So I went to see the patient and there were a few tents around but it was a lovely place with a stream running down beside them. In those days if the patient needed bed sheets, the midwife had to sign a form for what was necessary, because everything was rationed. This was the woman's sixth child and I said, "We must get a bed in here," and she agreed. We also needed sheets. So I signed what we called a 'dock' for the bed, sheets and blankets.

I delivered the baby and there wasn't a retained placenta, but there was quite a lot of bleeding and I had to phone for the doctor to go and have a look at her but she was fine. Every day I went out [to see her] on the tram car, and there was this little man, he was in the Registration Office and I always sat beside him. One day when I went on the tram the man was there as usual and he was laughing his head off and I said, "What is so funny about today?" He said, "The tinker was in yesterday to register her baby and called the baby after you." The woman had seen my name on the 'dock' and named the baby after me. I was quite pleased.

In those days we got a lot from the Red Cross in America, clothing, food, milk and other useful things, which we gave to people who needed them. Another nurse and I went out one night to the tents with a bundle of clothing for the children. They gave us what we thought were clothing coupons in exchange. And what we had when we came home was sweetie coupons! They lived on their wits and the exchange was for their own benefit – we expected clothing coupons that we could use for others. A while later I went out to the camp site to collect the grey army blankets that I had given her and there were posts in the ground covered with grey army blankets [to make tents]. I couldn't very well take them out of the ground.

Some nurses' empathy towards the travellers and the conditions they lived in, is illustrated by Dolina:

We had an unmarried girl in the tinker's encampment out in Marybank [outskirts of Stornoway], a lovely girl, and she wanted to be confined at home. At that time, we had two nurses in the area and it was the other nurse who was going to deliver the girl's baby. They had a hut so the other nurse was happy to deliver her at home. We happened to have had the decorators decorating the nurse's cottage and we had rolls of wallpaper left over, so all this went out to the hut and she got the men to paper it. Psychedelic, but at least it was clean and it was fine and we had everything in order for the confinement. The other nurse got them to tidy up around the house and it was just fine. One particular afternoon, the girl came to my door, weeping and crying, "I've been at the doctor and he says that I have to go into hospital. He says that I'll be better in hospital, but I don't want to go." I said, "Leave it at the moment, when the other nurse comes she'll speak to the doctor and don't you worry about it, it will be fine, come and I'll make you a cup of tea and I'll take you home."

I told my colleague when she came home, and off she went to the surgery and she said to the doctor, "What are you doing to the girl, what is wrong with her?" He said, "Nothing, but why should you have to work in these conditions, when she can get a hospital bed?" "If that is all that is wrong leave her at home, because I've gone to a lot of work to get the place ready," she replied. "What if you are going to be there for two nights or more?" asked the doctor. She replied, "We'll just have to cross that bridge when we come to it."

The girl went into labour and delivered very quickly with no problem. One or two days after the baby was born, I happened to be in the nurse's house in the morning, and I saw my colleague coming and she was pot black from top to toe and all I could see was the peaked hat she wore and I said to her, "What on earth happened?"

"I fell at the tinkers' encampment."

"Did you hurt yourself?"

"No, but look at the mess."

Two doors down I saw the doctor's car. I went chasing after him. I said to him, "Come, quickly, nurse has fallen."

"Where did you fall?" he asked her. She said "I fell out at the tinker's encampment."

"Serves you right, I told you not to go," he remarked.

These were the sort of things you couldn't do nowadays. We were younger then, you were ready to take on anything. You had the confidence to do it. The other nurse was able to carry on with her work after a good clean up. She wasn't hurt.

This incident appears to have taken place in the early 1970s when district nurses began to work in teams and had colleagues for support. Betsy Whyte believed that by the 1950s most travellers had settled into houses. She maintained that compulsory schooling for children after the war caused them 'much vexation and misery' as they had to live in a house for most of the year.

It is difficult to imagine the conditions that these nurses worked under and the challenges they faced carrying out their work. Maryann recalls attending at a delivery:

I was on my knees on the earth floor, delivering the lady. I used to go on my knees to deliver her as I had delivered her baby before. She was lying flat on the earth. There wasn't a bed and we were in a tent. We got water from the river. Everything went fine most of the time. I remember the last time I was there during the night and the doctor was there and he was getting so tired that he went away to get a flask of tea for us and when he came back he sent her to hospital. He was fed up sitting up there during the night. She got on fine, but I had to deliver on my own [the nurse would go into the hospital to deliver the baby]. I always sent for the doctor for the delivery but they weren't there very often. I was mostly on my own, but the patients liked to have the doctor booked.

The extract indicates that although the doctor did not have the patience to wait for the delivery, the nurse still had to be on hand to deliver the baby when she went into hospital. One can understand why this same nurse, Maryann, complained of feeling 'so tired that she was afraid she would fall asleep at the wheel of her car.' If she had a few overnight deliveries, and had to carry out her daily work as well, it would have been exhausting.

Most of the travellers were confined at home, as Dolina remembers:

> We had tinkers' encampments too and they were mostly all confined at home.
> It was amazing the effort they went to have everything in order. It was fine.
> The tinkers always had heating. There were no social workers or anything, but
> they survived and the children were always well looked after. They had their
> own way of working. Anything you used, such as a jug, or bowl, was put aside
> and was boiled. They were very fussy about that sort of thing. But the Tong
> Road group seemed to be a better class, because I remember going there to do
> a post-natal visit. I hadn't delivered her. But they always had fresh clothes for
> the baby every day, and the mother said to me, "I'm sorry nurse; nobody came
> in to do the ironing". I said that is not important, that doesn't matter.

It is clear from Whyte's book that travellers had to cope with a great deal of ignorance
and prejudice from the community. What Dolina's perception or experience of the
travellers was is unknown, but she indicates surprise at the cleanliness of the house
and that the mother had someone 'coming in' to carry out her ironing. It is also clear
from all the extracts that the travellers looked after themselves and their children.
They were also kind to the nurse who cared for them as Christine describes:

> I remember the tinkers at Tong Bridge. It would have been 1957 or 1958 and
> I was called out. The doctor came in to tell me that there was an un-booked
> patient at Tong Bridge in labour, so I had to go there. It was her first baby, and
> I was there most of the night and the baby was born early morning. The doctor
> came to see the woman since she wasn't booked and stayed until the baby was
> born. The family treated me very well, but you could hardly move, everybody
> came in to see the baby. It was a hut they were in. There were two rooms and
> I remember there was a youngish woman there and she made a meal for me.
> I didn't like to refuse it; I was hungry as I had been there for a long time. The
> food was alright, it was a big 'fry up' and I remember onions being there anyway
> and I couldn't take onions for a long time after that. They treated you very well.

*Travellers' camp.
(Highland Photographic
Archive, Inverness
Museum & Art Gallery,
High Life Highland)*

Whether the nurse cared for the patient in a tent, a shed, on a bed or the floor it was accepted as normal. The travellers, who may have been lacking in material possessions, were described empathetically by the district nurses. Their cleanliness, care of the baby clothes and their kindness to the nurses may have given the latter a different perspective of the kind of people they perceived them to be.

Even in the twenty-first century there are striking differences in the health of the travelling people when compared to other ethnic minorities. In 2007 in England it was found that travelling people were more likely to have long term illness and higher than average rates of miscarriage and premature death of offspring. Reports of the Confidential Enquiries into Maternal Deaths covering the period 1997–2007 identified travellers as having the highest maternal death rate among all ethnic groups. If the travellers in the twenty-first century have health problems, it is possible that there were similarities some fifty years ago. The supervisor who cautioned Morag that the 'tinkers have retained placentas' may well have experienced problems with them at confinements.

CHAPTER NINE

Pushing the Boundaries

Village street with telephone box in Ness, Isle of Lewis

Beyond the Call

It has long been recognised that a nurse's work is flexible. However in the period from the 1940s to 1970s it is questionable whether the nurse had clear boundaries of care. It would appear that professional 'crossing the line' only came under public scrutiny in the decades since the reorganisation of the Health Service in 1974. It may be that in the past district nurses undertook aspects of patient care that some felt was beyond the professional boundaries of their role because the district nurse knew the patients in their own homes. The nurse was aware of the problems that would not have been seen by hospital staff or GPs. Consequently, her knowledge of her patients created a moral obligation to provide care. The following accounts outline circumstances in which nurses undertook what would be regarded today as non-nursing care. These incidents raise questions about the clarity of district nurses' role boundaries in the period.

Nurses refer to the various roles they fulfilled which at a later date would have been the remit of other health professionals. Neilina recounts:

> In the days when we were on the district you did triple duties. I remember once counting the amount of duties that I had done in twenty-four hours. I had done the health visitor's job, by that time if there was a health visitor she wasn't available. I did my own job, and I did the chiropodist's job. I remember in the

93

care unit this old lady she was ill and I went and did the return visit there. I went to bed and I think about 1 o'clock in the morning the phone rang and this was a man with retention of urine and it was a terrible night. There was snow on the road, it was terrible and I went in to see him and I phoned the doctor. The doctor said that the roads were bad, so I said I'll pass a catheter, which I did. I had done it dozens of times in the Western Infirmary in Glasgow, but when I came back to work as a district nurse that was the doctor's job. I came back home, went to bed and I wasn't in bed for an hour when somebody rang that the old lady had died. Now today that is the undertaker's job but that was really the true position in those days.

Mary accepted the various roles she carried out as meeting the needs of her patients:

Sometimes you made a spot of creamola or something like that. You might be attending an old couple and it would probably be the *bodach's* [old man] only chance while you were in to get out of the house and go to the well to fill the pails of water. The *cailleach* [old lady] had been sprogged up and I knew he would have to do the washing and would have to collect the water. In those days the stoves weren't all that good for cooking or heating the water.

This lad came from hospital and they decided he needed daily baths after a rectal operation. There were five houses in that street and none of them had baths. You got a big tin bath, I remember it distinctly, and it must have been about 1970. The family had a tap outside the house. You would take the water and boil it inside and fill your bath. They usually had good big peat fires but we had to measure the water, so as not to be extravagant. I never did domestic chores in a patient's house and was never asked to.

The Queen's Nurse magazine included 'Invalid Recipes' from 1946–1957, for dishes which many district nurses at that time may have made, and given the recipes to their patients (see Appendix 2). Nurses therefore had the knowledge to look after their patient's nutrition and to use the ingredients that were available at the time. Making the patient a pudding may well have been considered within the nurse's remit at the time – courses in 'sick room cookery' were included as part of general nurse training. If the nurses were taught to manage the patient's nutrition they would consider it within their scope of practice.

With the development of social care services after the 1970s home helps carried out household tasks and it would be the role of the auxiliary nurse or carer to bath patients. It would be the remit of the dietitian to look after the patient's nutrition. Despite this, nurses still carried out care beyond the call of duty on occasion, as Catriona recalls, 'There was somebody who was quite ill and they had a lovely garden so I just went and did the garden, but that was off my own bat, I wasn't asked to do it, but you know you got involved. I did it just as a friend.'

Mary didn't hesitate when called to assist with a lamb: "A man's lamb had a broken leg and he asked if I had any bandages I could put on the lamb's leg, which I did'. Chris also maintains that, although she was never asked, 'I have seen me going to old people and make them a cup of tea and do things like that, but that was a voluntary thing, people didn't ask you to do that, but I have done plenty of that and the *bodachs* often asked me to "fill my pipe"'.

It would appear that nurses could be involved in many different tasks, but they suggest that they were not expected to go beyond their nursing duty. On one occasion Catherine was annoyed with the permanent nurse whom she felt had gone beyond the boundary of nursing:

> I used to take the shopping with me in the morning for one older lady, as a matter of fact I think that was the only one, and I offered to do it myself. I never lit a fire in a patient's home or anything like that. I washed clothes for one patient but it was the permanent nurse who started it and I did it when I was relieving. I wasn't happy about that. I remember one Christmas Day I came home with a pile of urine soaked bedclothes and my son, who was just

Sick Room Cookery Certificate, 1950

a small boy, was looking forward to his Christmas dinner and here was me coming home with this smelly load! He was standing up against the wall and how disappointed he was. Everybody else is having a Christmas dinner and what are we going to get! They were big flannelette sheets too. I had to wash them before Christmas dinner! Nobody would do it nowadays.

Roles and Responsibilities

A study carried out in 2000 on the role of district nurses on the mainland found that non-nursing tasks were influenced by the rural-urban split, with the rural nurses being more likely to help with domestic chores than the city nurse. This was not the case in the Outer Hebrides, where most nurses do not recall being asked to do household chores or carry out what may have been considered non- nursing duties, such as shopping for patients. Some nurses occasionally made a cup of tea for a patient who lived alone, but were never asked to do so. Many nurses felt that poverty was worse on the mainland, as Lena describes:

> If patients couldn't manage some household chores like lighting a fire they would ask me – that of course was in Glasgow. I did that often and also ran to the shops if there was no food in the house. In Uist you would never do that. Oh no, you would probably make them feel 'Does she think we can't do it?' But in Glasgow you could run out to the corner shop to get shopping if the husband was working. I found more poverty in Glasgow.

Lena's experience was echoed by other district nurses working on the mainland. Ida Sowler, in her autobiography recalling her time as a Queen's Nurse in Gullane, East Lothian in the 1930s and 1940s mentions encountering similar expectations that she should attend to every household chore in a patient's home. She was only able to use her full nursing skills when she was given a car and was able to extend her practice to surrounding areas.

In the 2000 study of mainland district nurses the performing of non-nursing tasks was considered to be 'a defining characteristic of district nursing'. In the Outer Hebrides, this was true to a much lesser extent, however even there non-nursing tasks were not an issue because things which may be perceived as being beyond the boundary of care today were accepted as part of the nurses' role at the time. Catriona remembers: 'I used to do quite a lot of physiotherapy with the stroke patients until they were quite mobile. We had to do bed bathing, general nursing care, washing people, as I say cutting toe nails, and cutting patient's hair, nowadays nurses don't do that as it is the role of the physiotherapist, carers and podiatrists.'

There were no community physiotherapists in the Outer Hebrides in the 1960s, therefore the nurse considered it part of her role. Similarly, there would be no chiropodist or carers to carry out the personal care. As has been noted, in many areas, particularly the smaller islands, nurses also distributed the medicines.

Up until the 1970s nursing textbooks included treatments for various conditions, including physiotherapy where appropriate. Male catheterisation procedure was also included in the textbook, which indicates it was part of the nurses' training.

With the reorganisation of health care in 1974 a wider range of health professionals was introduced to the islands and some dissatisfaction about role boundaries was evident, as was noted in the relationship of nurses to health visitors. Problems over boundaries between the roles of health professionals began to appear as Nora, who worked on an island with no doctor in the late 1970s, recalls:

> When I think of the psychiatric nurse … arguing with him because he would never come down here and I would tell him, "Do you realise that I am doing your work, two nights during the week I have been up doing your work and you never budge from your home." There were people with mental health issues because of alcohol problems which kept me very busy at times.

District nurses cared for all people across communities. Mothers and babies were part of their caseload, as were schoolchildren, ethnic groups such as the travellers and anyone else in the community who needed their care. The nurse's practice may have been similar to her counterpart in a city, though somewhat extended, but her support network was very different and much more informal. The knowledge nurses relied on to address their patients' needs would of necessity be extensive, yet the moral component of their knowledge is apparent, and it was this that could influence them if they had to cross the boundaries of their work.

Some nurses carried out unconventional treatments, which may have been part of the culture at the time. This could also have been a response to limited resources and a need to improvise. Care decisions were not obviously underpinned by evidence based practice at the time of the study.

Because the nurses were mostly lone workers they recall carrying out care that today would be the remit of other professionals. There was no-one else to provide it and they perceived that they had knowledge in most areas of care. Many nurses were adamant too that they did not carry out non-nursing care, hence it is clear that what they considered to be appropriate nursing work was encompassed within very wide boundaries. The district nurses of the Outer Hebrides describe addressing their scope of practice confidently and competently, with their focus on providing the best service they knew for their patients.

CHAPTER TEN

Babies and Death

Nurses often had to transport their patients in a rackety bus

Autonomy and Midwifery Practice

It was necessary for nurses to act autonomously and make decisions for themselves, requiring little support or supervision, because they were involved in care that was sometimes unpredictable and urgent.

Midwifery care was a large part of all the nurses' work and most of them stated they enjoyed this part of their role. The 1940s and 1950s were known as 'the golden age of midwifery' because midwives were competent and confident and worked as autonomous professionals. Until the late 1960s most births in the Outer Hebrides were confined at home. In the 1970s the number of home births had decreased considerably and the role of the district nurse changed. The Annual Report of the Medical Officer of Health for 1972 indicates that only eight home births were carried out in Lewis and that, 'in the last decade births were considered to be an Institutional event.'

After the 1970s mothers could still request a home birth, despite the Peel Report which stated, 'we consider that the resources of modern medicine should be available to all mothers to allow for 100% hospital delivery'. In response to the Report, the Association for Improvement in Maternity Services (AIMS) campaigned for the right of a woman to decide where to give birth. An added impetus to the campaign was the result of an analysis of mortality rates between births at home and in hospital.

It was shown that planned home births for normal pregnancies were safer than hospital births, provided experienced midwives, who knew the mothers, cared for them. Midwives advocating the provision of home births argued, along with the statistician who carried out the research, that home births were safe. Nonetheless home births have reduced nationally since the 1970s. One nurse, Margaret, tells of the premature baby she delivered on the road while out on her visits: 'It was so small that I had to feed it four times a day. I used to walk through the crofts with my wellingtons on to the mother's home as there was no road to the house. The baby thrived.'

Nurses had the obstacles of distance, inadequate transport and poor road conditions to consider when patients had to travel to get to the hospital for treatment of obstetric emergencies. Roads have now improved and help can come quickly, yet midwifery emergencies will always occur in remote areas. Although this chapter focusses on emergencies, Mary puts home deliveries in perspective, 'Having deliveries at home was so common that it was a natural thing to happen.'

Many nurses had experience of managing women with complex midwifery deliveries. Of the nurses who feature in this book, five had experienced the delivery of a stillborn baby, two delivered a breech presentation, two delivered twins, one delivered triplets, two cared for a woman with an ante-partum haemorrhage and another managed a woman with a post-partum haemorrhage. Some nurses' experienced complex foetal presentations while others delivered a baby who had abnormalities.

Morag recalls a day in 1952 which she will never forget:

> It was the day the King died and it was a very windy day. I was at a confinement, it was her third child, and the delivery went fine. The baby had a spinal abnormality and I found it very hard to tell the mother that the baby wasn't right. When I told her she was very distressed and insisted that we get the doctor. There were no phones except in my cottage so I ran home and phoned the doctor. He was in bed with the flu so he asked me to phone another doctor in another area but I couldn't get him at all. I then phoned back the local doctor and he said, "There is nothing for it, you will have to take the baby to the hospital in Stornoway." The mother seemed relieved but she didn't understand the extent of the child's problem and that very little could be done. We all got ready and we got a fishing boat to take us to the mainland. We had a long walk to the shore. I got a travelling rug from my mother to wrap the baby in and off we went. It was so stormy! When the boat reached the mainland we were met by an awful ambulance, if you could call it that, as it was just a run-down old van. The journey to the hospital took over an hour and the baby was admitted. On the way back it was so stormy that I could hardly get a fishing boat from the island to collect me to take me back. The baby was sent to the mainland but there was little they could do. The mother nursed the child for many years and he died in his teens. She looked after him so well and his skin was perfect when he died. She did have another child after that. I knew nothing could be done for the baby but I had to respect the mother's wishes and get any help that was possible.

There were five midwifery beds in the Stornoway Hospital in the 1960s – not enough according to some of the nurses. Some district nurses, who at that time were also all midwives, indicated that periodically they had to spend time in the hospital to keep their skills updated. They were also required go into the hospital with the mother and deliver the baby if hospital admission became necessary. Dolina recalls:

> I was doing night duty in the Lewis Hospital and this doctor came in. He said, "I need a bed." I said, "I don't have a bed for you, we only have five beds and we have a patient in the labour room bed … there are no beds, but a single room that the surgeon wants for a patient that is coming in tomorrow for a caesarean section."

> "Give me that bed," he said.

> "But he'll kill me if I give you that one". Well, he said, "Come with me and see where the midwife is working. She is out in a tent [in the travellers' camp] and the Tilley lamp has gone out and there is no paraffin and the rain is coming in. The trainee doctor is sitting on a sink pail ready to go through the floor anytime." I said: "Well if I take this patient off the labour room bed I'll have to put her on a trolley, is that girl nearly [ready to deliver]?"

> "She is quite near."

> I said, "Bring her in." The nurse, I'll always remember her coming with her wellingtons on in the middle of the night. She got the patient onto the labour bed; got her delivered and the next morning she went home.

Stillbirths

The conditions that nurses worked in were often challenging and they managed them as they thought best at the time. Maryann had to deal with a distressing experience:

> I had two stillborn babies. One was quite unexpected but the other one was expected. One of them had hydrocephalus, and had been dead in the womb for quite a long time and before the doctor could get the forceps on, what a carry on we had. I was giving the anaesthetic which sometimes happened. We just couldn't get [the forceps] on and the whole bed went to the floor. The bed collapsed. I'll never forget that, mind you it wasn't to the fore until now. I'm shaking now when I think of it! We were all on the floor but not too far down, it was quite a low bed, and the poor doctor was just [on relief duty] at the time. It was a horrible child. It was hard trying to hide it all. I didn't want to let [the mother] see it. No, she didn't see the baby. She wouldn't want to see the baby it was better for her not to see that, the huge head. The other stillbirth wasn't expected [but] the doctor was there. [Births] were over by the time the doctor arrived quite often.

In the late 1940s when this incident took place there would be no debriefing for the nurse after the stillbirth. It shows the considerable strength of character required of these women as they were expected to cope with any situation. Confidentiality was important to the nurses and it may have been that the nurse had not spoken of the first incident since it happened some fifty years before, as she told of 'shaking as she thought of it.'

It has been suggested that nurses have to 'mask' feelings of abhorrence in order to help mothers come to terms with foetal abnormalities. This nurse's attempts to prevent the mother from seeing the dead baby also indicates the prevailing attitude of the time towards abnormalities in children. Judy Fryd, who gave birth to a child with severe learning difficulties in the 1940s, encountered such prejudice that she was instrumental in founding The Royal Society for Mentally Handicapped Children and Adults, now known as Mencap.

Mary tells of her experience with a patient who also had a stillbirth:

> I remember a lady who had three boys and her husband had come home as she was expecting her fourth child. He was working away from home. She sent me a very worried message to come and see her. I couldn't get a foetal heart. When the baby was born I discovered that her waters had gone some time before and the baby was dead and it was a girl. That really shattered me. It must have been dead at least a couple of days, but she hadn't gone into labour. She realised when she started labour that there was something wrong. When the baby was delivered it had a very short cord, which was something that wouldn't happen today without being noticed, probably a scan would have detected it. I found it very sad. It was a trainee doctor that came out and she was so distressed that the [doctor] came and knowing the family he asked the mother if she had any idea that anything was wrong and she replied that she hadn't felt the baby moving for a few days. I remember that there was some question that the doctor would like a post mortem and her husband heard this. When I went back to do the return visit a bunch of men with a tiny little coffin were leaving from the house, and I found that quite awful.

Like Maryann, Mary was a lone worker and did not have colleagues with whom she could share her experience. She was more concerned with how the family coped than with her own feelings. Although Mary described herself as being 'shattered' at the outcome of the birth, there was no suggestion from her that she held herself responsible. Indeed the accounts suggest that none of the stillborn babies mentioned were injured at the delivery by poor midwifery care. It would appear that most stillbirths were due to circumstances outwith either the nurses' or the patients' control.

Haemorrhage and Retained Placentas

Nurses describe being confident in their own ability but were aware of the complexities associated with birth, particularly when they worked alone in remote areas without a hospital nearby. Morag recounts her experience when working on the mainland of Scotland. Her patient had suffered a post-partum haemorrhage and this affected Morag's confidence:

> I had one haemorrhage in Glasgow, and the patient had to be transferred to hospital. I said to the superintendent, "That's me finished."

"Why?" she asked.

"Because the patient had a haemorrhage."

"Who's afraid of the haemorrhage?" she asked.

"I am," I said, "And I'm finished."

Despite her frightening experience Morag did not 'finish' but continued with her career, including maternity care. When she worked on a small island in the 1950s, she had another harrowing experience:

> I had a lady with a retained placenta and I sent for the doctor. He came and it was quite a stormy day. The fishing boat came to take the lady to the mainland as she had to go to hospital. We put the patient on a door improvised as a stretcher, on the boat and she was sea sick and with the sea sickness more clots would come away. I shall always remember the herring scales in the boat and the smell! It was terrible. Doctor and I were there and the crew and her father and her husband. At the pier there was just an old bus improvised as an ambulance to take us to the hospital over an hour away. When we arrived at the hospital I put my face to her face and she was quite cold and nearly pulseless then. She was put onto the trolley and she was to go directly to theatre. The blood transfusion was started right away and when about half a pint of the bottle went in she came round and asked for the bed pan. The placenta came away beautifully. What a relief I can assure you. I think if there was an answer to prayer ever, then it was that day, because we were all in an awful state and that is one case that I will always remember, praise the Lord. She was home in two or three days.

This scenario reveals the clinical emergencies that district nurses in the remote islands encountered and the limited services available to deal with them at the time. It illustrates the variable and often urgent nature of the work the nurses carried out and how they played a pivotal role in managing the care and treatment of patients. The acceptance of this situation as part of her work was evident. The emotional turmoil of the journey and the severity of the woman's condition are described as worrying for all involved. The story demonstrates the nurse's strength of character and her reliance on her faith. Despite the worry about complications in midwifery the same nurse stated that, 'although I say it myself maternity was my best, I liked it very much.'

Rebecca describes her experience with an ante-natal patient with a haemorrhage, which she found frightening:

> It was the woman's third baby and she had lost the first two. She had a bad obstetric history. We had a trainee doctor and he was called out and, before he phoned me, he had got the patient into the ambulance ready for going to hospital some forty miles away. It took me about ten minutes to get out of bed and get my bags. It was about five o'clock in the morning and the patient was in the ambulance. Of course once I got in, the ambulance just set off. I didn't

have time to examine her, but I stood beside her and felt her contractions and we hadn't gone far when she started having expulsive contractions. I told the ambulance driver to stop while the baby was being born. It was a hair raising experience. Having lost two babies already! The baby was born; the placenta came out but then she started bleeding. That was really scary and [the driver] just put his foot on the accelerator and we got her into hospital. I packed her vagina on the way to stem the bleeding. The mother and baby were alright but it was quite alarming. I blamed the trainee, because he should have known how far on the lady was in labour. Perhaps I should have just put my foot down and said I am going to examine her before I go with her in the ambulance but I took it that he had done that. I was a trained midwife, but delivering a baby in the back of an ambulance, with a bad obstetric history too … that was one really scary experience I had.

Even though the outcome for the patient and baby was positive, the nurse was able to reflect on what had happened and what she should have done, instead of accepting the trainee doctor's word about the patient's condition. The Myles Textbook for Midwives maintains that 'only in remote areas will the midwife have to cope with a traumatic haemorrhage alone.' The situation was an obstetric emergency and the nurse revealed that she had the knowledge to cope with it successfully.

Complex Foetal Presentations

Anna describes her experience of attending a woman in labour:

She seemed to be in second stage, but she wasn't having second stage pain and eventually we realised that something was wrong. I examined her and it was a hand that I felt. It was the worst experience I have ever had. The doctor was in the kitchen with the husband. He gave her a quarter of morphine and we went off to Stornoway. I was terrified that her pain might start, but it didn't. She slept most of the time. … the doctor must have gone to the post office and telephoned the hospital and we were expected. We went in [to the hospital], she was almost asleep. The pains had gone fortunately for her. The doctor and the sister were waiting. The sister turned the baby so quickly into a breech and delivered it, a girl, a lovely girl. I was so sorry it was stillborn. But then the sister started shouting, "Fundus, fundus, this woman is starting to haemorrhage," and we managed to stop it. We rubbed up the fundus. I didn't actually deliver a stillborn except that one at the hospital. I was crying on the way back home – it was a bad experience, very bad.

It must be remembered that most of the nurses would have been in their twenties or early thirties at that time and were lone workers with no-one with whom to share their experiences. The nurse's journey back to her home would have taken her about two hours and she would have immediately gone back on duty, probably without discussing the incident with anyone. The nurse described providing all the medical care she and the doctor could in the circumstances.

Nora recounts her experience of delivering a breech baby when she was concerned about complications:

> The day I delivered a breech I sent the husband to tell the doctor to come and that it was urgent, because I was afraid of complications. [Everything went] fine, I panicked maybe to begin with. You always tried to keep yourself so that the patient wouldn't notice that you were too worried. But to me my faith meant a lot to me. I don't think I would have gone through my nursing from the first day I left home until today without my faith. To me I felt that I could lift my head and see Maggie Myles' book on the wall, and even the pages were turning, with each thing that I did to deliver the baby and the baby was delivered. I was cutting the cord when the doctor appeared outside the door and everything was ok.

Twins

Obstetric ultrasound scans now used worldwide were first developed by Professor Ian Donald in Glasgow in the late 1950s. Prior to that, nurses and doctors relied on their own examination of the mothers to diagnose multiple pregnancies. At times the diagnosis of twins was uncertain as Mairi recalls:

> I had a set of twins one was born on the Tuesday afternoon and the other was born on the Wednesday morning, they were ok. I was with her all that time. I had the doctor coming in and out. I had managed to get a hold of him. I had examined her in the morning and I felt a foot, so I sent her husband to get the doctor. I didn't want to start delivering a breech on my own, but that was what it was, it was twins. We didn't know they were there [but they were both] ok.

This birth was seemingly uneventful for the nurse. She went on to say she had delivered another set of twins and 'they were fine'. Multiple births were exciting if there were no complications, as Rhoda describes:

> I delivered twins in Shawbost when I was there, twin boys. It was very exciting, because the lady had boys and she wanted girls. Her mother was with her in the house when the babies arrived; we had a good idea it was going to be twins, and I had notified the doctor. The first baby arrived and the doctor then came and said, "Another boy!" and the mother said, "Oh don't tell me!" and the *cailleach* was not amused, she said, "Be quiet, you should be thankful that they are alive." She was annoyed at her daughter complaining when they were alive and well.

Pain in Labour

In the 1960s and 1970s various publications advocated the relief of pain in childbirth using various methods relating to the mother's attitude and confidence during labour. Sheila Kitzinger, a well-known childbirth writer, stressed the value of antenatal preparation for birth and the importance of the environment surrounding the birth.

She maintained that the environment where the birth took place could either reduce or contribute to the perception of pain. Most of the nurses here did not consider pain as an issue in labour. Many suggest that pain is something that the media has introduced into midwifery in the last twenty years.

Morag is quite scathing about present day midwifery services:

> I never used drugs. I went to Raigmore Hospital for the gas and air training, but I don't think I ever used it much here. ... I think it is ridiculous. They all go to hospital. Of course there must be two midwives and a doctor on hand today and I can't understand it. I was trained. But before that, local women went round delivering babies and they were good too. I think that practical experience teaches far more. Certainly you need the theory, but I believe in practical experience and that is why I can't understand nurses now when they start going to universities, I believe in practical experience in the wards.

Effie did not consider pain in labour a problem: 'The doctor was always available to help if there were any problems and that didn't happen very often. Women did not have painkillers and they didn't complain. It was left to nature's way.'

Anna also agreed that pain was not a problem in childbirth at home:

> Eventually we got some gas and air. I would say 1948 or 1949. No pain relief [was needed], but the women were strong. I think on the whole, because they were fit, they worked hard, croft work and taking home peats, they were very fit really. I think it did help the labour.

Myles' Midwifery Textbook, with which all Scottish midwives were familiar from the 1950s to 1970s, asserts that the midwife's personality and attitude plays an important part in the behaviour of the woman in labour. Similarly, as was noted, it was believed that the environment of the birth can have an effect on the pain. It is possible that the combination of the physical and emotional strength of island women as observed by the midwives, and their confident approach, could have had an effect on the mother's perception of pain, however there is no evidence regarding the latter at this time.

Last Offices and Maternity Care

As already mentioned, one of the duties of the district nurse was the laying out of a dead body. This occasionally conflicted with maternity care as both duties could not be carried out because of the risk of infection. In addition it was not permitted by the Local Supervising Authority (LSA), an organisation set up in 1915 in Scotland under the Midwives Act of 1902, and consolidated in subsequent legislation. The LSA's role was to exercise general supervision of midwives and it was required to notify them of various circumstances related to midwifery. One such situation was the period immediately following the laying out of a dead body.

Mary tells of the problems related to this required notification:

> As time went on we worked it out. If you had a hospital discharge, mother and baby, you didn't attend them for a day or two days afterwards because you

were like the lepers of old, you were contaminated. Once you touched a body, you were contaminated! You didn't care for babies for two days.

Anna found it difficult to refuse to attend a patient: 'If somebody died in a house, they would send for the nurse. You weren't supposed to [attend a death] if you had a maternity case but I never liked to refuse. There was no one else.' Chris too found this rule a dilemma: 'You had to go out if a patient died at night. If I did I had to report it and had to be off duty from babies for forty-eight hours, I tried to avoid that if I could.'

It is understandable that a lone worker would have problems balancing the needs of terminally ill patients and pregnant mothers. It seems that nurses got round this dilemma by trying to avoid touching a body, as they would then have to notify the LSA and would not be allowed to attend to a birth or care for a baby.

Decision Making

Decision making is a key element of community nurses' assessment in practice, and often the challenges they face are different from those of their hospital colleagues. Along with challenges in the assessment of patients, nurses in the remote areas of the Outer Hebrides faced problems with accessibility of medical services, as well as transport difficulties. Each area was geographically different and some nurses worked more autonomously than others, especially if the doctor was not easily accessible. Nurses carried out decision-making on a daily basis, and it is doubtful that their clinical decisions were based merely on experiential knowledge, as several nurses have mentioned the importance of their nursing textbooks.

On the smaller islands where the nurse was first on call and had therefore to diagnose, they were responsible for decisions. All the nurses in this book were trained midwives as well as trained general nurses. Christina was aware of her responsibilities regarding clinical decisions: 'I did the antenatal as it was laid down; I was very fussy about it, because there were home deliveries then. You had to be very careful because you were the one who was going to be landed in the middle of the thing.'

For Chrissie H the Midwives Rules were forever in her mind, as she had had to write them out in verse during her training in 1939. Christine describes an unusual occasion when she had to make a decision about whether or not to attend a patient:

I had one unusual call out. A man who had gone berserk and they were trying to calm him down. He must have taken too much alcohol. It was during the night; I didn't refuse to go. I think probably it should have been a police case. When I got there he had calmed down. He was saying that he was going to commit suicide. I think it was the effects of drink.

Christine's own personal knowledge of the community may have been a factor in her attending the patient. She stated that: 'The patient had phoned the doctor but I don't think he wanted to get involved.' It was ironic that the doctor did not attend the patient, however the nurse defended him, saying that he did not want to be involved and that 'she had phoned him and it ended up all right.'

One nurse spoke about receiving a call that would have required different kinds of knowledge from various sources:

> I was called to a person who had shot himself. I couldn't touch him until
> the police came so I had to pacify everyone around. There were quite a few
> people. And then the doctor came and he couldn't touch him either as we still
> had to wait for the police. I had been taught how to deal with situations like
> that. You were taught that in lectures at Queen's. But you were able to cope
> with anything and everything at that age.

The nurse knew before she went to the patient what had happened but it did not deter her from making the decision to attend the call. She was confident in her ability.

For nurses who worked on the smaller islands it was not just the nursing care that they had to make decisions about. Rebecca recounts a clinical decision she had to make:

> I remember one night called to an elderly lady with severe pain that I took
> to be cholecystitis. She had a history of this condition. There was a howling
> gale, the boats couldn't get out, the ferry wasn't running and really she
> needed to see the doctor, so he asked me to visit the patient. He prescribed her
> morphine. We kept these dangerous drugs in a locked cupboard in the clinic. I
> gave it to her. It was a terrible worry until he got down the next day.

Although the nurse diagnosed the patient's problem she was not confident and needed reassurance from the doctor. Whether her decision was influenced by experiential knowledge or medical /practice knowledge is unknown.

Nurses on the smaller islands had the added responsibility of being on first call, accessing the ferry as well as other transport if the patient had to be hospitalised. However, where midwifery was involved, nurses took responsibility for making decisions and did not depend on the doctor as Mary explains:

> Largely … you were a practitioner in your own right when you were a midwife
> and the doctor probably didn't see a person until she was seven months
> pregnant. He would probably know the string of babies she had before that
> or if [it was a first baby] he would have a peep and see just how well she was.
> … if you got into trouble, you called the doctor. If you knew that somebody
> had started in labour, maybe a young one, you would give the doctor a ring
> and say, "I might have to call you later in the night," but if not the baby was
> delivered normally and you phoned when you came back home.

In their role as midwives the women had no qualms about making independent decisions, but when carrying out general nursing work they recall often referring to the doctor. It was unusual for the GP to contradict the nurse or vice versa, but on one occasion Jean did not hesitate to make the right decision for her patient:

> When I got to the house they had been working on it and there was no outside
> light and I got in only to find this girl in labour. She had never told us, never
> had any antenatal care and this was her second. She didn't want to go to
> hospital. She didn't tell anyone and there was nothing in the house. I knew

she was well established in labour just by looking at her. I examined her and she was dilated and there was no way we could have made it to Stornoway 60 miles in the night! So the doctor came in and says, "She'll have to go hospital." And I said there was no way she could go to Stornoway. I was not delivering in an ambulance halfway there in this weather. We [would] either lose the baby or both. It [had] to be a home confinement. He hummed and hawed and I said there was nothing else for it. The ambulance was at the door waiting to take her away and I said, "No, she can't go," so that was it. I tried my best in the house but there was nothing ready and the house was in a *boorach* as they were working on the house. A safe delivery of a girl.

This nurse overruled the doctor by not allowing the patient to be sent to hospital and appeared to make the decision based on her midwifery knowledge, her personal knowledge of the area and for the safety of the mother and baby. Jean goes on, 'You decided if they needed a doctor. It was quite a responsibility on an island. You had to decide, say just now if you thought you needed hospital or a doctor and a ferry had to be called out. You had all those decisions but I felt confident to deal with them.'

Maryann describes the reason for the call-outs she received: 'It was busy and it was really a big district. There were very few things that you weren't called to even if you had to send for a doctor. They would call the nurse first. There were not many accidents. There was very little traffic on the road for which I was thankful.'

Peggy a'Bhard. (Comunn Eachdraidh Nis)

Although there were few accidents to attend it was expected that nurses would be called out to whatever ailment or injury presented itself on the district. The nurse would contact the doctor after she had assessed the situation. Rebecca speaks of making decisions and how glad she was when she moved to the town area to work, where she could easily access a doctor. One experience she remembers:

> There was this baby and he wasn't well and I kept phoning the doctor and it was late at night. I phoned him and I thought surely he'll come now and you know this; he didn't. He didn't come until morning and by then that baby had to be rushed away. These were the terrible decisions. I had to make them on the spot. I think we took a lot of the doctor's work on. I must admit when I got a temporary job in Stornoway on the district, I thought I was in heaven, there wasn't the same worry. There was a lot more nursing and heavy nursing, but not the worry of ferries and doctors. It was wonderful for me.

Rebecca was the only nurse who appeared to have concerns working on an island with no doctor and with communicating with the doctor.

Unknown circumstances did not deter these informed women from attending to patients or relatives. Their knowledge of the area and the people may have helped them to cope with difficult situations. They appeared resilient, continuing with their work after some difficult experiences and responding at times to calls without considering the personal consequences.

Some of the complexities of midwifery that the nurses experienced were clinical emergencies. Several did not have a positive outcome, such as when a baby died. The effect of traumatic experiences on the nurses is unknown, yet one nurse, some fifty years after the event, was 'shaking' as she thought of it. Confidentiality was important to the nurses, and they did not have colleagues with whom they could share their experiences.

The responsibility to mothers and the babies was immense and nurses accepted responsibility in obstetric emergencies. At times they indicate that they were afraid and anxious about a situation, particularly in midwifery, yet seemed to portray confidence that may have come from their knowledge of what to do in any given situation. Queen's Nurse training was acknowledged by some nurses as being highly relevant to their practice and some attribute their ability to manage any situation to this training.

In their role as midwives, nurses were competent and confident in making decisions; the criteria for being an autonomous practitioner. Their accounts describe then as taking personal and professional responsibility for their practice without regard to their own wellbeing. Their resilience and strength of character in the face of setbacks was evident.

CHAPTER ELEVEN

From Kentucky to the Outer Hebrides and Back

Mary Breckinridge on horseback

The Frontier Nursing Service

Unlikely as it may seem, the inspiration and the model for establishing a
community nursing and midwifery in Kentucky in the United States came from
the Hebrides. Mary Breckinridge, an American nurse, was keen to find a model for a
new nursing service she was planning in the remote areas of Kentucky in the 1920s.
She was concerned that America was decades behind Europe in training midwives
and district nurses. More women had died in pregnancy in the USA than American
men had been killed in war up to that date. Training for midwives was virtually non-
existent and maternal mortality was four times higher than in parts of Britain well
served by Queen's Nurses.

Breckinridge, who had trained as a midwife in London, was impressed by the
skills of nurses on the mainland, particularly in Hertfordshire and Perthshire. By
the autumn of 1924 she was very keen to see the new system in action in Scotland.
She contacted Sir Leslie Mackenzie, a medical member of the Dewar Committee
and a key architect of the Highlands and Islands Medical Service, which in her later
writings Breckinridge more correctly renamed the Highlands and Islands Medical
and Nursing Service. She also gave common currency to the term 'nurse midwife'
now widely used in the USA and other parts of the world.

Calling first at the Queen's Nursing Institute in Edinburgh, Breckinridge then embarked on an extensive tour of the Highlands and Islands to look for herself at the HIMS and the model of a doctor and a nurse working together in a geographical area. As well as the north of Scotland, Breckinridge travelled to the Outer Hebrides, where she met with district nurses, including Annie Maclean in Harris, referred to by the Dewar Committee (1912) as 'the overworked nurse from Harris'. Breckinridge found 'an exceptionally fine nurse living in a cottage hospital with a small operating room and accommodation for four to five patients.' Nurse Maclean provided midwifery and general nursing services for eighteen scattered villages.

"More than I can put into Words"

Breckinridge was overwhelmed by the warmth of the welcome she received. She also echoed the comments some of the nurses in this book made about islanders not suffering an extreme want of basic necessities, at least compared to the extreme poverty in cities. Only in Colonsay did she see a lack of warm clothing for children. Back in Edinburgh she hit the shops in Princes Street and sent up parcels of jumpers to the Colonsay minister.

Breckinridge took meticulous notes on her visit, filling eleven notebooks. Her experience in the Western Isles proved an epiphany. She later wrote:

> The time had come when I must leave the Hebrides. I have tried to tell what they meant to me. To the Frontier Nursing Service, in after years, all that I gathered from these islands was to mean more than I can put into words. Sometimes an experience is so deeply creative that you respond to it with everything that you have, not only in retrospect but at the time. When I went to Scotland in mid-August of 1924 to make a study of the Highlands and Islands Medical and Nursing Service, I knew that weeks of enchantment lay ahead of me, but I could not know until it happened what it would be like to enter a strange country and feel at once that I had come home.

Significantly, Breckinridge added '... and Nursing' to the Highlands and Islands Medical Service title. And she was right – nursing was what the Dewar Committee had identified as being the most urgent need. Her goal became to transfer the whole idea to Kentucky.

Back in Kentucky she set about organising what became the Frontier Nursing Service (FNS). One of the first priorities was the need for an epidemiological study of Leslie County to establish the population's health needs for mothers and children. Sir Leslie Mackenzie provided the right candidate, a Miss Bertram Ireland who, along with her colleague Dr Mary Menzies, had carried out a similar special study for Mackenzie in 1917 in the Outer Hebrides. Miss Ireland was also already working in the USA, could ride a horse (the only method of getting around) and could take a nickname – standard procedure for those who joined the FNS. She became 'Ireland from Scotland'.

Such was Breckinridge's appreciation of all she found in Scotland that she invited Sir Leslie and his wife Helen to open the first FNS hospital in 1928. It was an arduous journey for the not-so-young Mackenzies. They were welcomed by one of the British midwives who made up most FNS staff; Queen's Nurse Ann Mackinnon from Skye, and a war heroine (awarded the Croix de Guerre for her courage as a nurse under enemy fire in France in 1918). Breckinridge said:

> Annie P. Mackinnon from Skye was one of our early recruits. She had served with the French Flag Nursing Corps during World War One and was awarded the Croix de Guerre for conspicuous bravery in continuing to care for the sick and wounded under enemy fire during the retreat from Aisne in the early summer of 1918. Inevitably in Kentucky she was given the name 'Mac'.

On lecture tours Helen Mackenzie later encouraged Scottish nurses of an adventurous spirit to join the FNS. She and her husband were strong advocates of a wider movement to improve the

Ann of Appalachia (as she was known) on her mule Tenacity. (Photo courtesy of Frontier Nursing Service, Hayden Hospital, Leslie County, Kentucky, USA)

health of poor mothers and children, a passion shared by their friend Elsie Inglis, a Scots doctor who established an eponymous hospital for women in Edinburgh.

Helen Mackenzie was also a lecturer and (later chair of governors) of the Edinburgh School of Cookery, which later became Queen Margaret University and today offers a range of nursing courses. The sharing of good nursing practice across the Atlantic has continued. In 2000, the Family Health Nurse, a new community nurse model, was piloted in the Outer Hebrides with some of the theory originating from America. This new role was seen as multi-faceted and generic and the community nurse's work included helping individuals, families and communities cope with illness and improve their health. That a new model of nursing was required was recognition that something had changed in district nursing. It was suggested that the 'new' FHN model was reminiscent of the kind of relationships that district nurses claimed to have had with their patients in the past. Unfortunately, the FHN did not continue within most communities.

The challenges facing district nurses and midwives in remote and rural communities do not recognise international boundaries. They were – and they remain – universal.

Bibliography

Abel-Smith, Brian (1977) *A History of the Nursing Profession*. London: Heinemann Educational Books Ltd

Anthony, M.J. & Barkell, N.P. (2008) Nurses' Professional Concerns: Letters to the Editor 1900–2005. *Journal of Professional Nursing*, Vol. 24, No. 2, pp.96–97

Baly, M.E. (1987) *A History of The Queen's Nursing Institute: 100 Years 1887–1987*. London: Croom Helm

Baly, M.E. (1991) *As Miss Nightingale Said....* London: Scutari Press

Baly, M.E., Robottom, B. & Clark, J. (1989) *District Nursing*. Oxford: Heinemann Nursing

Banfill, B.J. (1953) *Labrador Nurse*. Canada: Ryerson Press

Barker, A. (2011) *Remembered Remedies: Traditional Scottish Plant Lore*. Edinburgh: Birlinn Limited

Beech, B. (2006) At Last: An NMC Home Birth Circular. *AIMS Journal*, Vol. 18, No. 1

Beth, Mary (1995) *Healing Threads: Traditional Medicines of the Highlands and Islands*. Edinburgh: Polygon

Bingham, S. (1979) *Ministering Angels*. New Jersey: Medical Economic Company

Bloom, A. (1953) *Toohey Medicine for Nurses*. Edinburgh & London: E & S Livingstone Ltd

Breckinridge, Mary (1981) *Wide Neighbourhoods: A Story of the Frontier Nursing Service*. The University Press of Kentucky, pp.188–190

Brief General Report of the Medical Services Boards Nursing Scheme for Lewis and Harris for the Year 1917–1918. Western Isles Archives, Stornoway

Briggs, Asa (1972) *Report on the Committee on Nursing*. London: HMSO, p.1

Caird, B.J. (1972) *Changes in the Highlands and Islands of Scotland 1951–1971*

Cathcart Report (1936) *Committee on the Scottish Health Services Report*. Edinburgh: HMSO

Census Scotland, Gaelic Report 1951, 1961 and 1971. General Register Office, Edinburgh: HMSO

Clark, D. (1982) *Between Pulpit and Pew*. Cambridge: Cambridge University Press

Cohen, S. (2010) *The District Nurse*. Oxford: Shire Publications, pp.8–11

Cowell, B. & Wainwright, D. (1981) *Behind the Blue Door: The History of the Royal College of Midwives*. London: Ballière Tindall Cassell Ltd

Crossfield, M.L. (1973) The Lewis Hospital Stornoway: Some Aspects of the Development of Medical Care in an Island Community. *Medical History*, Vol. 11, No. 1

Dickens, C. (1844) Martin Chuzzlewit in Calder, J.M. (1963) The *Story of Nursing*. London: Methuen's Outlines

Dingwall, R.W.J. (1977) Collectivism, Regionalism and Feminism: Health Visiting and British Social Policy 1850–1975. *Journal of Social Policy*, Vol. 6, pp.291–315

Dingwall, R., Rafferty, A.M. & Webster, C. (1991) *An Introduction to the Social History of Nursing*. London: Routledge

Doig, Dr., cited in Ferguson, C. (2006) *Children of the Black House*. Edinburgh: Birlinn Limited, p.245

Donnison, J. (1999) *Midwives and Medical Men: A History of the Struggle for the Control of Childbirth*. London: Historical Publications

Dougall, R.E. (2002) *Perceptions of Change: An Oral History of District Nursing in Scotland, 1940–1999*. Thesis, RCN Archives, Edinburgh

DN 150 (2008) Queen's Nursing Institute, Edinburgh. (Published to celebrate 150 Years of District Nursing)

Elstad, Ingunn (2006) *District Nursing Between the Local and the International, Northern Norway 1890–1940*. Stein Rokkan Centre for Social Studies Report No. 4. University of Bergen, pp.173–186

Ferguson, C. (2006) *Children of the Black House*. Edinburgh: Birlinn Limited

Ferlie, J.P. (1964) Historical Survey of Midwifery in Scotland. *International Journal of Nursing Studies*, Vol. 1, pp.125–129

Gardner, J. (1966) *Infant and Perinatal Mortality in Scotland*. Vital and Health Statistics Analytical Studies

Geoforum 12/72, Department of Geography, University of Glasgow, W2 Scotland

Gibb, P. (1992) District Nursing in the Highlands and Islands of Scotland 1890–1940. *History of Nursing Journal*, 1992/93, p.327

Girdwood, R.H. (1966) Some Problems of Nursing Today. *British Medical Journal*, 4th June

Hallett, C., Madsen, W., Pateman, B. & Bradshaw. J. (2012) 'Time Enough or Not Enough Time!' An Oral History Investigation of Some British and Australian Community Nurses' Reponses to Demands for 'Efficiency' in Health Care, 1960–2000. *Nursing History Review*, Vol. 20, pp.131–161

Health Visiting Survey 1984, Western Isles Health Board Working Group

Hegney, D., McCarthy, A., Rodgers-Clark, C. & Gorman, D. (2001) Why Nurses are Attracted to Rural and Remote Practice. *Australian Journal of Rural Health*, Vol. 10, pp.178–186

Highlands and Islands Medical Service Committee (1912) (Dewar Committee): *Report to the Lord Commissioner of His Majesty's Treasury*, Vols 1 and 11. Edinburgh: HMSO

History of NHS (2008) www.nhs.history.net

Horne, J.L. (1971, 1972) *Annual Report of the Medical Officer of Health*. Ross and Cromarty, Public Health Department, Dingwall

Information from Roland Stroud (2009), uncle of Katie

Leap, N. & Hunter, B. (1993) *The Midwife's Tale*. London: Scarlett Press

Lewis Hospital First, Second and Third and Fourth Reports from 1896–1900

Lewis Nursing Service Sub Committee of the County Council for Ross and Cromarty 1933–1947, Western Isles Health Board Archives, 21st September 1944

Loudon, I. (1991) On Maternal and Infant Mortality. *Social History of Medicine*, Vol. 4, No. 1, p.72

Matheson, A. (2000) *Notes on Nursing in Stornoway and Lewis Hospital from 1880*. Newton, Stornoway, Private Collection

McCrae, M. (2003) *The National Health Service in Scotland Origins and Ideals 1900–1950*. East Lothian, Scotland: Tuckwell Press

McGann, S., Crowther, A. & Dougall, R. (2009) *A History of the Royal College of Nursing 1916–90: A Voice for Nurses*. Manchester: Manchester University Press

McIntosh, T. (2012) *A Social History of Maternity and Childbirth: Key Themes in Maternity Care*. London: Routledge

Myles, M.F. (1971) *A Textbook for Midwives*. Edinburgh and London: Churchill Livingstone

Oakley, J. (1983) *Changing Cultures: The Traveller-Gypsies*. London and New York: Cambridge University Press, pp.18–19

Parry, G., Van Cleemput, P., Peters, J., Walters, S., Cooper, C. & Thomas, K. (2007) The Health Status of Gypsies and Travellers in England: A Population-based Study. *Journal of Epidemiology of Community Health*, Vol. 61, No. 3, pp.198–204

Pillitteri, A. & Ackerman, M. (1993) The 'Doctor-Nurse Game': A Comparison of 100 Years 1888–1990. *Nursing Outlook*, May/June 1953, pp.113–116

Queens Nursing Archives, RCN Edinburgh

QIDN (1944) *Fifty Sixth Annual Report, Scottish Branch, Castle Terrace, Edinburgh*. Darien Press, RCN Archives, Edinburgh

Report of Nursing Scheme 1917, 1918, 1934: NHS Western Isles Archives

Robson, M., ed. (2003) *Curiosities of Art and Nature: A Description of the Western Islands of Scotland*. Isle of Lewis: The Islands Book Trust, p.23

Royal College of Nursing Rules (1950) The Central Midwives Board for Scotland Archives/489/7/7 Edinburgh

Skár, R. (2009) The Meaning of Autonomy in Nursing Practice. *Journal of Clinical Nursing*, Vol. 19, p.226

Smith, P., School Records for Barvas, 1940s, Barvas, Private Collection

Speed, S. & Luker, K.A. (2004) Changes in Patterns of Knowing the Patient: The Case of British District Nurses. *International Journal of Nursing Studies*, Vol. 41, pp.921–931

Stocks, M. (1960) *A Hundred Years of District Nursing*. London: George Allen & Unwin Ltd

Sweet, H.M. & Dougall, R. (2008) *Community Nursing and Primary Healthcare in Twentieth Century Britain*. Oxon: Routledge

Western Isles Health Board, Health Board Working Group (1984) Health Visiting Survey. Western Isles Health Board Archives

White, R. (1985) *The Effects of the NHS on the Nursing Profession 1948–1961*. London: King's Fund Publishing

Yuginovich, T. (2000) A Potted History of 19th Century Remote Area Nursing in Australia and in particular Queensland. *Australia Journal Rural Health*, Vol. 8, pp.63–67

Appendix 1

Midwifes' Rules in Verse

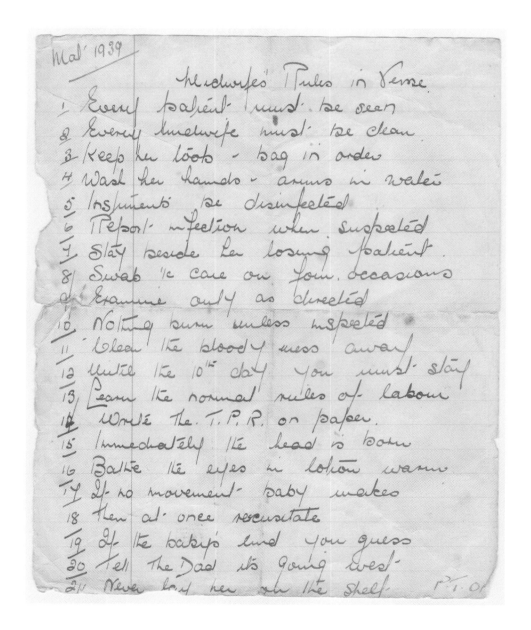

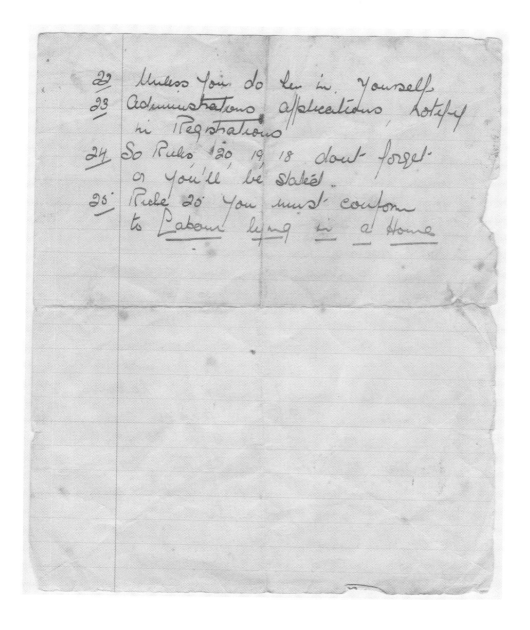

22 Unless you do ten in. Yourself
23 Administrations applications, Lotify
in Registrations
24 So Rules 20, 19, 18 dont forget.
or you'll be staked.
25 Rule 25. You must conform
to Labour lying in a Home

Appendix 2

Recipes from the Queen's Nurses' Magazine
1946–1957

Hot Potato Dogs | 1946

6 medium well scrubbed potatoes
6 sausages (skinned)

Remove a centre core, using an apple corer, from the centre of each potato, and stuff the cavity with sausage meat. Bake the potatoes in their jackets in the usual way. Serve hot.

Fricassee of Tripe | 1946

Tripe is often available, and if the patient likes it, is very suitable for an invalid.

¼ lb dressed tripe
½ oz margarine
¼ pint milk and stock
1 dessertspoonful chopped parsley
Small onion
½ oz flour
Seasoning

Wash and cut up tripe. Cover with water and bring to boil. Drain. Cover with stock or fresh water. Add salt and onion, finely sliced. Cool very gently until tender. Strain.

To make the sauce, melt margarine, add flour, and blend over the gas and gradually add ¼ pint liquid. Bring to boil, stirring all the time and cook for three minutes. Season. Reheat tripe in the sauce, and lastly add parsley.

Corned Beef and Raisin Sandwiches | 1946

4 oz corned beef – flaked
2 oz seedless raisins
1 tablespoonful mayonnaise
Bread and margarine

Pour boiling water over raisins, allow to stand for 10 minutes, drain and chop. Mix with corn beef and mayonnaise. Spread between buttered slices of bread, cut into fancy shapes and serve garnished with parsley.

Junket | 1946

Warm ½ pint milk to blood heat. Pour into a glass dish and stir in 1 teaspoonful of essence of rennet and teaspoonful of sugar. Set in a warm place. This is a good stand by as it is so quickly made. Children like it sprinkled with grated chocolate.

Apples in Hiding | 1946

Peel and core 3 or 4 apples; cut into quarters. Drop into a Yorkshire pudding batter just before putting into the oven. See that the batter covers the apples. Serve very hot, with sugar or golden syrup.

Potato éclairs | 1948

1½ oz flour
½ oz margarine
⅛ pint water
1 reconstituted egg
3 tablespoonfuls mashed potato
Seasoning

Melt the margarine in the water and bring to the boil. Remove from the gas, add flour immediately and beat until the mixture thickens. Beat in the egg, and if necessary add a little extra water to make the mixture quite soft. Beat in the mashed potato, put the mixture into a forcing bag with a half inch pipe and force onto a greased baking sheet. Bake in a moderately hot oven for about 35 minutes. Slit open and fill with a savoury mixture.

A New Way with Rabbit | 1948

1 dressed rabbit
1 pint water
1 sliced onion
½ teaspoonful pepper
2 oz fat
½ pint vinegar
3 oz sugar
2 teaspoonfuls salt
1 teaspoonful pickling spice
2 tablespoonfuls flour

Cut the rabbit into serving pieces. Mix together vinegar, water, sugar, onion, seasoning and spice and pour over the rabbit. Soak for 36–48 hours. Drain and wipe dry. Heat the cooker, put in the fat, fry the rabbit pieces till golden brown, and ¼ pint of the pickling liquid. Bring up to pressure, cook for 15 minutes and cool normally (i.e. allow pressure to come down without putting under the tap. Thicken the gravy with flour.

Oatmeal Dumpy | 1952

Melt in a frying pan: 2 teaspoonfuls fat. When hot, add to this: 2 teacupfuls coarse oatmeal, 1 medium chopped onion, ½ teaspoon salt, shake of pepper. Toss for ten minutes until golden brown and serve hot.

Benito Sweet | 1956

3 egg whites
1 egg yolk
Juice of 1½ lemons
Grated rind of 1 lemon
¼ oz gelatine
½ pint water

Dissolve gelatine in water. Add sugar, beaten yolk, juice and rind of lemons. Whip whites of egg until stiff, fold in all the other ingredients whilst still warm. Pour into decorative glass dish and decorate with whipped cream and slices of crystallized orange and lemon when cold.

Ginger Beer | 1956

4 quarts water
1 tablespoon ground ginger
½ oz yeast
2 lemons
1 lb sugar

Peel the lemon rind very thinly and add to the water with the juice, sugar and ginger mixed together. Bring to the boil, cool and when lukewarm, ferment for 24 hours with the yeast. Take off the scum and remove the lemon rind. This is an easily made drink with a slight fizz and a favourite of the children.

Gooseberry Sherbert | 1956

1 lb gooseberries
1 lemon
1 quart water
4 oz sugar

Cook the gooseberries in the water until very soft. Put grated lemon rind and sugar in a jug and strain the boiling liquid onto it. When cold strain through muslin. A delicious drink for hot days.

Kromeskies | 1957

8 oz mixed white meat
¼ pint thick brown or tomato sauce
Seasoning
8 thin rashers of bacon
½ pint fritter batter

Season the meat and mix it with the sauce. Divide into 8 and roll in cork shapes. Wrap a piece of bacon round each and dip batter and fry.

About the Author

The author while she was carrying out her
midwifery training in Thornhill Hospital, Renfrewshire

Catherine Morrison is typical of the nurses in this book. She completed her General nurse training in Glasgow and subsequently worked as a staff nurse in the Southern General Hospital before training as a midwife in Renfrewshire and then carrying out Queen's training in Edinburgh. Her year's secondment from Queen's was in Fallin, a mining village in Stirlingshire. She then spent six years working in neurosurgical nursing in Canada before returning to Glasgow to take up a ward sister's post in the Neurosurgical Unit. After some years in Glasgow she took up a post as district nurse in Bernera, on the island of Lewis, which had a bridge but no doctor. Catherine continued working as a community nurse, becoming community manager and latterly a teaching fellow at Stirling University Campus for nurses in Stornoway. In 2008 she won the Royal College of Nursing's UK Community Nurse award for initiating an overnight nursing service.

In 'retirement' she has pursued academic interests through distance learning and become a Volunteer Visitor for QNIS, supporting and befriending retired Queen's Nurses of the Outer Hebrides. She spent time interviewing nurses in the Outer Hebrides for her University of Manchester PhD. This book is an edited version of Catherine's PhD thesis which was written under the supervision of Professor Christine E. Hallett and Dr Hannah Cooke at the UK Centre for the History of Nursing, University of Manchester.

The Islands Book Trust

Based in Lewis, the Islands Book Trust are a charity committed to furthering understanding and appreciation of the history of Scottish islands in their wider Celtic and Nordic context. We do this through publishing books, organising talks and conferences, visits, radio broadcasts, research and education on island themes. For details of membership of the Book Trust, which will keep you in touch with all our publications and other activities, see *www.islandsbooktrust.org*, phone 01851 830316, or visit us at the address below where a good selection of our books is available.

The Islands Book Trust, Laxay Hall, Laxay, Isle of Lewis, HS2 9PJ
Tel: 01851 830316

www.islandsbooktrust.org